TO CATCH A PLAYBOY

TO CATCH
A PLAYBOY

BY

ELIZABETH DUKE

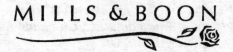

MILLS & BOON

MILLS & BOON and the Rose Device
are trademarks of the publisher.
Harlequin Mills & Boon Limited
Eton House, 18-24 Paradise Road,
Richmond, Surrey TW9 1SR
This edition published by arrangement with
Harlequin Enterprises B.V.

© Elizabeth Duke 1995

ISBN 0 263 14417 8

Set in Times Roman 16 on 17 pt.
16-9601-60245 C

Printed and bound in Great Britain
by Mackays of Chatham PLC, Chatham, Kent

CHAPTER ONE

Delia and Julius Branson
Invite Andrew Carstairs and friend
to join them on board *Mistique*
on Australia Day, 26 January.
Enjoy the Harbour Regatta and evening
fireworks.
Lunch and dinner will be served aboard.
Meet Man O' War steps, Bennelong
Point,
9 a.m. sharp.
Disembark: midnight
Dress: smart casual

TESS sat bolt upright, staring in disbelief at the invitation Andrew had dropped on to the table in front of her. 'Julius Branson?' Her blue eyes flared. '*The* Julius Branson? The media tycoon?'

'Ah...a reaction at last.' Andrew rubbed his hands in satisfaction. 'You thought I was kidding, didn't you, darling, when I said we

were going on a harbour cruise with one of
the richest, most powerful men in Australia?'

'Mmm.' Tess gulped, still dazed at this
stroke of amazing luck. A personal invitation
from Julius Branson! Here was the chance
she'd been waiting for, hoping for, for weeks.
The chance to meet the elusive magnate face
to face.

And to think she'd almost thrown the invitation back in Andrew's face without even
reading it! He'd been so insufferably smug all
through dinner. Like a cat drooling over a
bowl of cream. He'd teasingly waved the invitation under her nose, holding it just out of
her reach until she could happily have stuffed
it down his throat. It amused him to play these
tiresome little games. And she simply hadn't
been in the mood to play along. She hadn't
even wanted to come to this snooty restaurant
in the first place.

As usual, Andrew had turned up his nose
at her own choice of venue—a quiet bistro in
North Sydney—and had insisted on coming
to what must have been Sydney's swankiest
restaurant. Andrew liked to project a certain
image, and choosing the right restaurant—
being *seen* at the right restaurant—was im-

portant to him. As important as choosing the right wine. Tonight's choice was Pouilly-Fuissé.

From the moment they'd sat down at their table, she'd known he was bursting to tell her something. His eyes had been bright with some hidden excitement. But she'd had no idea then what it was going to mean to her when he'd asked, 'How would you like to celebrate Australia Day on Sydney Harbour with me? On a luxury motor-yacht—a state of the art *mega*-yacht.'

Her response had been cautious. 'Whose boat is it?' Most of Andrew's acquaintances struck her as snobbish and shallow, interested only in making money and making their mark on the world, with a marked tendency to mix only with people they considered of use to them. 'One of your lawyer-friends? Or one of your high-powered clients?' Someone, no doubt, who could help him in his career, or whose company would enhance his image. Andrew didn't waste his time on no-hopers.

Andrew was a very ambitious young man, aggressively single-minded in his determination to rise to the top of the corporate law world. An achiever who liked to mix with like-minded people, especially if they could help him in his climb up the corporate ladder.

Not that she would ever condemn a man for being ambitious. She was ambitious herself. It was their dedication to their respective careers that had initially drawn them together. But lately she had begun to wonder if she and Andrew shared the same goals any more. While Andrew's ultimate goals, she was beginning to realise more and more, were material ones—power, success, money—her own had always been more idealistic. After seeing her mother suffer for years from painful, debilitating rheumatoid arthritis, she had chosen medicine as her career and had specialised in the rheumatic diseases, wanting to help others like her mother. Now she was a qualified rheumatologist, with her own consulting-rooms at a North Sydney medical centre. She felt she was genuinely helping people who *needed* help.

But with Andrew lately it was all self—all self-interest. He didn't seem to care about anyone else...except her, perhaps. And she sometimes wondered how deep his feelings for her went, and how much her status as a medical specialist had to do with her attraction for him. He certainly didn't seem to care too deeply about his clients—not as *people*. He only cared about winning...and success. And the fame and money that promised to roll in as a result.

'Not a friend *or* a colleague.' Andrew was delighting in being mysterious. 'Though I hope that one day...' He shrugged, his even white teeth showing in a brief, gloating smile. 'It's not every day one gets an invitation from such exalted quarters.' He slid a hand inside his immaculate grey jacket, his fingers lingering on what was inside.

'Exalted?' She groaned inwardly. She probably wouldn't know a soul on board.

'Our host, my dear Tess——' Andrew was practically licking his lips '—happens to be one of the country's richest, most powerful men. Normally he only entertains family and close friends—he's a very private person. So you can rest assured, my sweet, we'll be among a very select group of guests.'

Tess had visions of being bored witless. But she'd tried to look interested, for Andrew's sake. 'Well, go on...I can see you're dying to tell me.'

'Don't rush me.' With a leer, Andrew plucked the invitation from his pocket and dangled it just out of her reach, as if tempting her to try to grab it from him. 'I want to whet your appetite first, darling. Just imagine it— a champagne and seafood luncheon on the deck—a full three-course dinner in the evening in one of the sumptuous saloons—a chance to mix with some *very* influential people. And after dinner, back on deck to watch the fireworks over Darling Harbour... partying on until midnight.' He paused, eyeing her expectantly.

'Sounds like sheer luxury,' Tess agreed. Andrew would be in his element.

'I'd really like you to come with me, Tess.' His smiling eyes told her he meant it. But they also told her that he would go himself, re-gardless of whether she went with him or not. 'You must be dying to know whose boat it is.' His hazel eyes gleamed. 'Take a guess.'

She tapped an impatient foot under the table. 'Andrew, I hate these games. Just tell me.' She glanced at her watch. 'It's getting late.'

'Oh, well . . . here.' With a flourish, he dropped the invitation on to the table in front of her. 'Go on—read it.'

Her stunned reaction must have been all he could have hoped for. Her mind was still reeling.

'So even you, Tess, are impressed by the name Julius Branson.' Andrew was positively smirking. 'You're not as immune to power and money as you like to make out.'

She flicked a tongue over her lips. If she denied it, he might start probing, asking questions. And she couldn't tell him the truth—not yet. The secret truth she'd stumbled on only recently. She couldn't tell anyone—perhaps ever. It was far too delicate. Far too tricky. So all she did was shrug. He could think what he liked.

'So . . . you'll come with me, then?' Andrew leaned back, well-satisfied. Confident he'd won her over.

While part of her itched to wipe the smug look from his face by knocking him back, the rest of her was churning with a mounting excitement. Barely even trying to hide it, she nodded.

Julius Branson... A tiny thrill riffled through her. Her *father*. Or rather, the man who *could* be her father. The father she had never known, whose identity had long been a mystery to her.

Since learning his name, she had despaired of ever finding a way to get close to him. Julius Branson didn't mix with ordinary people. He was an extremely busy and powerful man, who always had his minders and his own kind of people around him to protect him from the masses. And she knew that she couldn't write to him, asking the question... or even requesting a meeting. What if it wasn't true? No... She had somehow to meet the man first—observe him, look for signs of a likeness, or for a reaction when she mentioned her mother's name. And then she would decide what to do or say.

She tried to sound casual as she asked Andrew curiously, 'How on earth did you wangle an invitation from Julius Branson? Have you met him already?' She held her breath.

'No,' he admitted. 'One of my clients arranged it.' He shrugged, as if it hadn't been too difficult. 'I'd mentioned to him that I went through law school with Julius Branson's son Piers.'

'You did?' Tess drew in her breath, realising that if what she'd been told about Julius was true, then Piers Branson could be her half-brother! She swallowed a lump in her throat. She had never known a brother or a sister. 'What's his son like?' she asked a trifle breathlessly. 'You never see pictures of either of them in the papers, do you?'

'Well, not often, no. Not when Julius Branson owns most of the newspapers and magazines in the country,' Andrew said drily. "The rival tabloids sometimes catch a fleeting shot. But the Bransons never pose for the cameras. They like to keep to themselves.'

'Oh?' she said encouragingly, wanting to hear more about them. Anything.

'You mightn't read much about them,' Andrew said, his mouth pursing, 'but you *hear* a bit of gossip occasionally... about Piers, at any rate.'

'What kind of gossip?' Tess asked quickly.

He frowned. Tess wasn't normally interested in gossip. Or in other men. 'You keep your eyes off Piers Branson,' he warned her. 'Besides, he's not your type. He's a playboy. He plays at everything he does.' His lip curled. 'He plays at being a lawyer. He plays around with his father's media business. And, above all, he plays around with women.'

She almost laughed aloud. Andrew wouldn't be warning her off if he knew that she and Piers Branson could possibly be brother and sister!

Andrew's frown deepened. He was plainly puzzled—put out—that Tess was not looking disapproving. Men of that type normally filled her with contempt. 'He's not Julius Branson's real son, you realise,' he told her, his jealousy prompting a note of spite. 'Julius and his wife couldn't have children, apparently. They adopted Piers and his sister Phoebe after their own parents, who were close friends of the Bransons, were killed overseas. Piers was about four, and Phoebe a year younger.'

Tess let her eyelashes sweep down over her cheeks as a shaft of disappointment pierced her. Not only at finding out that Piers Branson wasn't a blood relative after all, or his sister Phoebe either—not even a half-brother or sister—but at Andrew's statement that Julius Branson and his wife were unable to have children. What if *Julius* was the one at fault, the one who couldn't have children, and not his wife? If that was the case, then he *couldn't* be her father!

Her spirits plunged to her toes.

Andrew's voice, sharper than usual, cut into her thoughts. 'Why so downcast all of a sudden?' His tone was accusing. 'You're not feeling sorry for Piers, I hope, because he lost his parents as a boy? I assure you, he doesn't need your pity. Or anyone's. As Julius Branson's heir, he'll inherit everything one of these days. He and Phoebe. But Piers will be the one taking control of the Branson empire.'

She looked up at him, composing her features before meeting his eye. 'Well, good for him,' she said with a careless shrug.

Andrew's eyes searched hers. He still looked faintly puzzled.

She glanced away. 'Andrew, can we go now? I have an early start in the morning.'

Andrew's handsome brow was furrowed as he settled the bill and escorted her out. Tess wondered if he was starting to regret asking her to join him on the Australia Day cruise. Surely he couldn't be *jealous* of Piers

Branson, simply because she hadn't con-
demned him for being a roving-eyed playboy?

If he knew her at all, he'd *know* she would
never be interested in a man like Piers
Branson. He was the type she'd always despised! In fact, now that she knew Piers
wasn't—couldn't be—a blood relative, even
if Julius Branson *was*, she'd lost all interest
in him. Rich, idle playboys were absolutely
the last type of male Andrew needed to worry
about!

She was beginning to suspect that Andrew
didn't really know her at all.

Australia Day dawned, bright and clear, a
perfect January morning, perfect for a day on
the harbour. Tess had already put a lot of
thought and effort into what she would wear.
She wanted, for once, to be noticed. To catch
Julius Branson's eye. What she wore needed
to be suitably casual... but striking.

When Andrew picked her up at her modest
home unit in North Sydney, he whistled,
bowled over by this new Tess he was seeing.

Usually, when she wasn't wearing a figure-
concealing white medical gown, she chose
dark, sombre colours and flowing styles that

covered her feminine curves and at the same time minimised her height, and combs or a hair-band to tame her riot of bright Titian curls. Today she was wearing a stunning black and white top threaded with gold, the scooped neckline deep enough to reveal an enticing glimpse of creamy cleavage without being embarrassingly obvious. A woven gold belt showed off her narrow waist, and her ankle-length white trousers enhanced rather than hid her endlessly long, slender legs. Her Titian curls, free of combs or ties, were today tumbling in a riotous mass of gleaming red-gold.

'Tess, you're a knockout.' Andrew was looking at her as if he'd never seen her before. As if, she thought ruefully, seeing him square his shoulders and proudly thrust out his jaw, she were a prize trophy he was desperately keen to show off. She wondered for a fleeting moment if she'd made a big mistake. She'd only wanted to catch Julius Branson's eye— not create a false impression! She had never deliberately flaunted her looks before.

But it was too late to do anything about it now. Andrew was already steering her to his well-polished Volvo—strutting along beside her in a way that made her irritatingly certain he was going to stick close by her side all day, wearing her like a prize rose in his lapel! That would make it difficult for her to have a private word with Julius Branson. But at least she would have a chance to meet him...and observe him at close quarters. And he would have a chance to observe *her*. After that, it would be in the hands of fate.

Tess's gold bracelet caught the sun's bright rays as eager hands reached out to help her aboard. But it was the crowning glory of her vivid flame-red curls, dancing in a sunlit cascade to her shoulders, that attracted the eyes of the guests already on board. A murmur went up when her long slender legs stepped gracefully on to the deck.

As Andrew flashed his invitation at a uniformed member of the crew a dark-haired woman of about thirty, wearing a flower-patterned sarong, danced up to them.

'I'm Phoebe Branson—welcome aboard.'

Phoebe...Julius Branson's adopted daughter! Tess felt a twinge of regret that this bright-eyed, friendly-looking woman wasn't and never could be her real sister—her own flesh and blood. But even an adopted half-sister...

She felt Andrew's arm slide possessively round her waist. 'Andrew Carstairs,' he said in the rather pompous tone he assumed when he was anxious to make an impression. 'I was at law school, Phoebe, with your brother Piers.' He glanced at Tess. 'I'd like you to meet my close friend, Dr Tess Keneally.'

As Tess smiled into the young woman's dark eyes she felt like kicking Andrew. She was always reminding him to drop the 'Dr' at private functions. He only said it for effect.

'Couldn't be a better day for the harbour regatta!' Andrew gushed, bringing attention back to himself. 'Perfect Australia Day weather!'

Tess glanced round, wondering why Julius Branson wasn't the one welcoming his guests. Perhaps one of his friends had lured him away. There was already quite a crowd on board, and the spectacular yacht had at least three visible decks, and heaven knew how many saloons were hidden behind the windowed interior, let alone other rooms down below.

'I'm afraid my father can't be with us,' Phoebe said, and Tess's eyes snapped back to her. 'He's been rushed to hospital for an urgent gall-bladder operation. My mother Dee is with him. Piers and I are filling in as hosts...though Piers is late, as usual. My fiancé Tom's about somewhere.' She flicked a look round. 'Ah, here he comes. I'll get him to look after you—he'll make sure you're given some champagne.'

The next half-hour passed in a black haze of disappointment for Tess. Faces came and went, glasses fizzed with champagne, trays of hors-d'oeuvres breezed by, and Andrew was in his element, dragging her from one group to another, his face lighting up every time he spied a familiar face.

Eventually she retreated to the outer rail, and when Andrew tried to tug her away to meet someone else, she shook her head.

'You go—I'll just stay here for a while. I want to watch the ferry race.'

'Well, if you're sure...' He was already backing away.

'I'm sure.'

With a sigh, she turned her back on the other guests and leaned over the rail, tipping her half-empty glass of champagne over the side. She felt maudlin enough already, without plunging into an alcoholic depression as well. What a time for Julius Branson to get a gall-bladder attack! Not that she didn't feel sorry for him—she knew how painful the complaint could be—but why couldn't it have happened tomorrow? Or next week? She would probably never get another chance to get this close to him. What on earth was she going to do now?

She stiffened as she felt cool fingers touch her arm. Turning her head, she glanced up— to meet a pair of the darkest, wickedest eyes she had ever seen. For some reason her heart missed a beat.

He was tall, quite a few inches taller than she was. At almost five feet nine herself, she didn't often find men towering over her. His deeply tanned face was strongly carved and heart-joltingly attractive, made more so by the tufts of silky black hair that fell in spiky disarray across his brow. One dark eyebrow was raised, causing a roguish furrow in his brow.

'Let me guess,' he drawled, in a voice unlike any other she had ever heard, like softest

velvet, deep and beautifully modulated.
'You're a TV star.'

She gave a brief smile and shook her head.
'I've never been on TV in my life.'

His lips curved in a smile as roguish as his
arched eyebrow. 'Well...let me guess again,'
he said, undaunted. 'Film star? Photographic
model?'

Tess stifled a sigh, feeling vaguely disappointed that he was no different from other
men she'd met for the first time, assuming
that she made use of her looks rather than her
brain.

And then she saw the brimming laughter in
the black eyes. She eyed him speculatively.
Was he just saying what he thought a woman
wanted to hear? Did the women he normally
mixed with lap up that kind of approach? She
grimaced inwardly. Maybe she *deserved* it, for
dressing to draw attention to herself!

And maybe he deserved some of his own
medicine!

'Let *me* guess,' she countered, tilting her
head at him, her blue eyes picking up the glint
of the sun. 'Used car salesman?'

The black eyes flickered under her sardonic
gaze. Then, abruptly, he laughed, his smile

widening appreciatively—a real smile this time, warm and genuine.

'*Touché*! I take it I'm not even close? Mmm...' His eyes gazed deep into hers, dancing black swallowing vivid blue. 'No... I should have seen it from the start. There's more to you—a lot more. Not just a pretty face. Humour... intelligence... a quick wit. A beauty with *brains*. Well, go on—tell me,' he invited, his tone only marginally contrite. 'What are you, then? A brain surgeon?' he asked teasingly.

'You're in the right field.' Her full red lips took on an ironic tilt. Male chauvinist, she thought. 'I *am* a doctor, as it happens. A rheumatologist, to be precise. That's someone who specialises in the rheumatic diseases,' she spelt out, her tone faintly mocking, deliberately giving him back some of what he deserved.

'You *are* a doctor? A *specialist*?' He stared at her. 'I don't believe it. You're too young.'

'I'm twenty-eight.'

'Piers, old man!' Andrew's voice sliced in from behind. 'Trust you to find my Tess!'

As Tess mentally rolled her eyes—I'm not your Tess, she wanted to flare back at him—

the name hit her. Piers! *Piers Branson*! She had been talking to Julius Branson's adopted son!

Andrew thrust out his hand. 'Good to see you again!' But his eyes, Tess noted, were wary as he glanced from one to the other. 'Has Tess introduced herself?'

'We hadn't actually got around to names,' Piers said smoothly. 'But we're already good friends. Aren't we...Tess?' His laughing eyes caught and held hers—for rather longer than was strictly necessary.

'Are we?' she said drily. She sensed instinctively that he was baiting Andrew deliberately—and Andrew, the big idiot, was asking for it, the way he was puffing himself up and all but glaring daggers at Piers.

'Dr Tess Keneally,' Andrew muttered in that infuriatingly precise way of his, his handsome face as stiff as his manner. 'Tess...I suppose you realise by now that you've been talking with our host—Piers Branson?' That womanising playboy, his eyes reminded her, urging her to keep it in mind.

He turned to Piers, shifting slightly so that he was partially blocking her from Piers's view. 'I'm sorry to hear about your father, old man. Guess you'll be expected to hold the fort, eh, while he's convalescing? If there's anything I can do—legal advice—anything...' He frowned faintly as Piers glanced past him. 'But we mustn't hold you up. You'll be wanting to move around, mingle...' His voice died away as Piers, stepping neatly sideways, caught Tess's hand and raised it to his lips. The pressure of his warmly sensuous mouth on her skin, its moist heat flowing into her fingers, sent a sharp, unexpected quiver of awareness through her.

'You must tell me more about yourself...later,' he insisted softly, before turning on his heel and losing himself in the crowd.

She found herself clutching the rail to steady herself, faintly dazed at the effect he'd had on her. Madness. She hadn't reacted like this to a male—in this pathetically mindless way—since she was a teenager! It just showed how right Andrew was about him—he was a shameless womaniser, a super-smooth operator...playing his role of rich, pampered playboy to the hilt. She was disgusted with herself. Philandering Don Juan types, charming as they might be on the surface, repelled her. Why hadn't she snatched her hand away instead of weakly standing there while he pressed his lascivious lips into her flesh? She could still feel the warm, moist imprint of them! How he must be laughing! He'd gone away well-satisfied, no doubt, that he'd made yet another easy conquest.

'*More* about yourself?' Andrew echoed, bristling. 'What have you been telling him? You seem to have become very cosy with Piers Branson in a remarkably short space of time. Did you tell him about *me*? Did you tell him we were practically engaged?'

Now she was the one who bristled. 'Certainly not—because it's not true! And you can stop acting as if I'm your property! I'm not! Oh, stop looking so sour!' She softened her tone, hiding her impatience—and a stab of guilt. 'We hardly had a chance to say anything. He was just trying to *needle* you, Andrew. Couldn't you tell?'

He thrust out his lip. 'You didn't have to let him smooch all over your hand like that!'

'Oh, Andrew, it didn't mean anything. It was just a bit of harmless fun. Men like him can't help themselves—they'll flirt with anyone.'

That *was* all it had been—just a bit of harmless fun. Piers Branson was plainly an incorrigible, irrepressible flirt, the type who didn't take life—or women—at all seriously. He'd never *had* to take anything seriously, with the money and privileges he'd had at his fingertips, being brought up as the Bransons' only son. And he'd wanted to make Andrew jealous. Purely for his own amusement, not because he was *interested* in her, for heaven's sake. If she'd felt something for a second, had fleetingly reacted to him, it was just that...she'd been momentarily flattered, that was all it was. It wasn't every day a man kissed her hand. Even Don Juans, much as she disapproved of them, possessed a certain charm. Especially *this* Don Juan, with his wicked, laughing eyes and his sinfully wicked mouth.

The memory of that sinfully wicked mouth pressing into her hand brought faint prickles to her skin even now.

'If you want to have fun,' Andrew growled, 'you can have it with me.'

She sighed. 'Then stop scowling. You're no fun at all when you're in this mood.' In fact, when she came to think about it, 'fun' wasn't a word she would have used in describing Andrew at all. He'd never had the greatest sense of humour. But he could be charming, in his own way, and considerate, and good company when he wasn't being pompous and trying to impress people. He was very clever, very bright. And he had the clean-cut good looks that any rising young corporate lawyer would have killed for.

'You're right.' Andrew smiled suddenly, glancing round as if checking that nobody else had caught sight of his scowls. 'Mmm, they're serving lunch. Wow...get an eyeful of those lobsters and king prawns! Coming?'

Tess found, as the day went on, that she was actually beginning to enjoy herself, despite the disappointment of Julius Branson not being there. The activity on the harbour was a constant diversion, with the sky-diving displays, the race of the tall ships, the aquatic procession and the other boat races, and every type and shape of spectator boat imaginable. The warmth of the late January sun on her face and the gentle breeze through her hair felt so delicious it made her realise how little leisure time she'd had in recent years.

Surprisingly, she even found herself warming to the other guests on board, finding most of them interesting, genuine people, prepared to talk on a range of topics. She particularly liked Phoebe Branson and her fiancé Tom Lloyd. Phoebe seemed very down to earth and natural, unspoiled by her father's money, or the Bransons' lofty position as one of Australia's wealthiest, most influential families.

Unlike her wicked-eyed playboy brother Piers.

Tess wasn't sure why she was so pricklingly aware of him. He kept bobbing up every now and then, smiling his wicked smile and tossing some light-hearted remark that brought an involuntary smile to her own lips and a forced one to Andrew's. Maybe she just *wanted* to think well of him because he was Julius Branson's son. If Julius did turn out to be her father then Piers, even though he wasn't a blood relative, would be the closest thing to a brother that she would ever know.

But—she bit her lip, a vague uneasiness stirring deep inside her—her reaction to him hadn't been at all a sisterly one. Far from it!

She heaved an impatient sigh. Well, how *could* she feel sisterly towards him? He was a complete stranger to her! And even if Julius Branson did prove to be her father, and admitted it to her, he would probably be vehemently opposed to letting his family know about her, after keeping her a dark secret for so long—let alone be prepared to acknowledge her publicly. He'd kept quiet about her, presumably, because he hadn't wanted to hurt his wife by revealing his past indiscretion. So he'd be unlikely to want to hurt her now, let alone suffer the scandal and embarrassment it could possibly cause *him*.

'Why the sigh?' asked Andrew, frowning. 'You're not getting bored, are you?'

'No!' Her denial was swift and emphatic. 'I'm enjoying myself. Tremendously.' It was true. For some reason, she felt more alive today than she had felt for ages.

The sparkle in her eyes convinced Andrew that she meant it. But at the same time it made his frown deepen. 'You're telling me you're getting a taste for the high life?' he asked sceptically. 'Or is it...the company on board?' His gaze slid away, to rest on the back of Piers Branson's dark head.

Tess pretended not to notice, determined not to let Piers Branson come between them. 'You're fishing, Andrew,' she teased, linking an arm through his. 'Of course it's the company. *Your* company.'

But *was* it? an insidious voice niggled.

CHAPTER TWO

IT WAS only later, when Tess was standing at the rail watching the evening fireworks soar and explode into the starry night sky over Darling Harbour, that she found herself briefly alone again, Andrew having excused himself to duck down below.

'Your fiancé's plainly the possessive type,' a velvety soft voice purred at her ear.

She felt a shivery thrill run through her. But when she turned to face the man standing behind, her expression was cool.

'Andrew is not my fiancé,' she said crisply, wondering at the same time why she was so anxious for Piers to know it.

'But you have an...understanding?' The wicked eyes challenged her.

She took a deep, careful breath. She ought to discourage him here and now by lying and telling him that they did. The spark of attraction she felt for him—yes, no use denying it, it was there—was no more than an ephemeral attraction that any girl would feel

32

for an attractive, amusing man. And today she was in the mood to let her hair down, for once. But she didn't want it to go any further. Piers Branson's reputation as a high-living, fun-loving playboy—a good-looking Lothario who loved to chase after women— disgusted her. His wicked eyes warned her to keep right away from him. He wasn't at all her type. And yet...

And yet, by catching his interest, by be-friending him, she might yet get a chance to meet Julius Branson. And she *had* to meet him—she had to know the truth! Even if he didn't *want* her to know. She was a mature adult. She wasn't likely to do anything stupid or rash. He need have no fear that she'd start shouting it from the rooftops. She wouldn't tell a soul, if that was the way he wanted it. She just needed to *know*.

'Andrew and I don't have an under-standing,' she said coolly. 'He'd like to—but so far...' She shrugged as she let the rest trail off.

'So you're not living together?'

She shook her head. Andrew would have liked that too, but up until now she'd resisted. She liked her own space, her own home, her independence. 'What's this—the third degree?' she murmured. 'Are *you* living with anyone?'

His white teeth flashed in a grin. 'Not right now, no.' A hungry light glowed fleetingly in the dancing black depths. 'So...the way is clear, is it?'

Clear? her heart skipped a beat. As she waited for her heartbeat to settle down she tilted her chin. So...he was ready to move in, was he? Andrew was right about him—he was nothing but a woman-hungry Lothario. If he thought...

She stifled her repugnance. This could be the opening she'd been hoping for. The chance to get closer to him...and ultimately to Julius Branson! She eyed him sideways, a provocative gleam in her eyes, deciding to play along with him. 'Would you worry if it wasn't clear?' she countered.

'Probably not,' he confessed shamelessly, and it was all she could do not to show her disdain. Andrew was right. He'd chase after anything in skirts! Or, in her case, leg-hugging trousers!

She lifted her chin a notch higher. 'I live in my own home, and Andrew lives in his. We lead separate lives. He...*has* asked me to marry him,' she admitted, her conscience pricking. If Andrew could hear her now, he'd think her no better than Piers! And maybe she wasn't...

'But you haven't said yes.'

'Not...yet.'

'But you're thinking about it?'

'No! I mean... Look, I'm not committed to Andrew or anybody. And I've made that clear to him. Is that what you want to know?'

Something flickered in the depths of his black eyes. For a fleeting second she would have sworn it was disappointment, or contempt even, rather than satisfaction. She felt a flare of dismay. Had she made herself too readily available? Men like Piers Branson— men who played around themselves— probably had double standards. They could play fast and loose, but they preferred their women to have more integrity. Maybe Piers liked his women to play hard to get.

Right, she thought. If that was the only way she could spark and hold his interest, then that was the way she would go.

She turned abruptly away. 'I'd better go and look for Andrew.'

'Why?' She felt her nerve-ends jump as his hand closed on her arm. 'I thought we were just starting to find some common ground.'

She swung back to face him. 'Common ground?' she echoed coolly, slanting her head at him.

'Yes. You're not committed . . . and neither am I. And as I happen to have a spare ticket to the gala charity performance at the Opera House on Friday night, I thought you might like to come to the opera with me.'

She drew in her breath. She couldn't remember the last time she had been to the opera. And never with Andrew, who always said it bored him to death.

'Ah! I see a spark of interest.' Piers's mouth curved with satisfaction. 'Glittering gala nights appeal to you, then?'

'Gala nights?' She had barely taken that bit in. 'Oh . . . yes, sure,' she said. If she admitted to him that glitzy social events like VIP gala nights left her slightly cold—so many people only attended because it gave them a chance to dress up to the nines and parade around, showing themselves off—he might change his mind about taking her . . . and she might never see him again. 'That means evening dress, I take it?' she asked airily.

'Well, sure—dress up as much as you like.' His tone was indulgent, but there was a thread of something else in his voice that wasn't so easy to read. 'We guys are expected to front up in black tie, so you go ahead,' he said expansively, 'and feel free to knock everyone's eyes out, if that's what you want. We'll be sitting in the front row of the dress circle, and there'll be a supper afterwards in the reception area overlooking the harbour lights.' He paused, watching her, his eyes narrowed to glinting slits of ebony.

Darn it, she thought. Now I've made him think I *want* to tart myself up and make a spectacle of myself, *want* to be seen gracing the front row of the dress circle! She smiled weakly. 'And the opera?' she asked.

'Oh, so you *are* interested in the opera too?' Now his eyes were laughing at her, mocking her. 'It's Offenbach's *Tales of Hoffmann*. Nothing too heavy, you'll be relieved to ——'

'Oh, but that's one of my favourite operas!' she cried impulsively. 'I have the recording on compact disc... with Joan Sutherland and Placido Domingo.' She eyed him curiously.

'You're not an opera fan yourself?' she asked. Was *he* only going because it was a gala event?

He shrugged. 'I don't often go. I've always preferred films and the theatre. I wasn't intending to go to this one...until I thought *you* might be interested in coming along.'

Luring her, she thought, with offers of a glittering gala night and the chance to dress up to the hilt. Her mouth tightened imperceptibly. How little he knew her! 'Well, it's very kind of you,' she said with a brief smile. 'I *am* interested. I love the opera. Not that I've had too many chances to go lately, I must admit.'

'Your work?' Piers queried, lifting a quizzical eyebrow. 'Or...Andrew not interested enough to take you?'

'A bit of both,' she admitted. Andrew would relish a gala charity performance though, she reflected with a faint twinge of guilt. Preening himself in the front row of the dress circle. Strutting around the foyer during the intervals in full evening dress. Hobnobbing with the rich and famous. He'd lap it all up. Trying his best not to fall asleep during the actual performance!

'We mightn't stay long at the post-opera supper.' Piers's tone was silky. 'Unless *you* want to. These suppers tend to turn into bun-fights. I'd rather have a bite to eat somewhere quiet...where we can sit down and enjoy ourselves.'

Just the two of us, he meant. Her mouth went suddenly dry. Where, precisely, did he have in mind? And what did he have in mind...for later? Was he expecting something in return for the evening he was offering her?

Best to lay some ground rules right here and now.

'Well, a quick bite, maybe, if it's not too late,' she said with a shrug, avoiding his eye. Eye contact might give him the idea she was giving him the green light. 'I start work early in the mornings.'

'You work *Saturdays*?' He tilted his head at her.

She let her gaze flutter away. Damn! She had forgotten it was a Friday night. 'Next Saturday morning I am,' she lied. There were times when she did go in to her rooms on a Saturday morning, mainly to catch up on her paperwork.

'Oh, too bad... Then you won't be able to come sailing with me on Saturday.' She could hear the amusement in his voice, sense the wicked eyes mocking her. He didn't believe her. He was trying to call her bluff, *tempting* her, trying to see if she would change her mind. Thinking, no doubt, that she was playing a clever little game of some kind. A game of hard-to-get...in the hope of sparking his interest!

Her brow puckered faintly. She had always been honest and up-front with people. She had never indulged in games, preferring to have things out in the open, to get straight to the point. Besides, she'd never had the *time* to dither and dance around playing games. But... She swallowed, feeling a breath of disquiet. Wasn't that precisely what she'd been doing? Playing a little game of her own? Hadn't she been using her feminine wiles to catch Piers Branson's interest? Wasn't she playing up to him now, *using* him, in the hope of meeting his father? And—she might as well admit it—enjoying every disreputable minute!

'No...sorry,' she murmured. 'Well, I——'

'You'd better give me your address and phone number,' Piers intervened smoothly, before she could move away. He pulled a small black book from the pocket of his trousers.

Typical, she thought, trying not to show any reaction. Men like Piers Branson always have little black books! I wonder how many other women's names he's got listed there already! Each one appraised, no doubt, on a scale of one to ten!

As Piers was jotting down her phone number Andrew reappeared.

'Sorry I took so long... Someone grabbed me on the way back.' His hazel eyes were fixed on Piers's little black book. Like Tess, he was doing his best not to show any reaction. But his very stiffness spoke volumes.

'Not to worry,' Piers said easily. '*I* grabbed Tess! She's been in safe hands, I assure you.'

'Thanks,' Andrew said, almost through clenched teeth, as if he thought Piers about as safe as Little Red Riding Hood's wolf.

'Piers has kindly offered me a ticket to the opera on Friday night,' Tess put in casually. There was no way she was going to go behind Andrew's back. And she wanted Piers to know it. 'You know how I love the opera . . . and it's *Tales of Hoffmann*, which I adore,' she added, keeping her tone light. 'I don't often get the chance to go.'

'Especially not to a gala charity performance, I gather,' Piers put in smoothly.

Tess sucked in her breath. Damn it, why did he have to tell Andrew that? Did he know Andrew that well? Know that, to Andrew, the thought of missing out on a VIP gala night, with all its glitz and glamour and famous celebrities, would rile him more than missing out on the performance itself? Was he deliberately trying to make Andrew jealous?

She frowned into the wicked black eyes. But the object of her frown simply flashed an easy smile and drawled, 'Excuse me . . . I'd better do my hostly duty. We'll be going ashore in a few minutes.'

'Now that *I'm* back he remembers his hostly duty,' Andrew muttered darkly as Piers swung away. His hand clamped on Tess's arm, none too gently. 'What's this about you going to a gala opera performance with him? Don't you know his reputation? Is it just the two of you going?'

She looked pointedly at the hand clasping her arm, not answering until he'd slackened his grip. 'Which question do you want me to answer first?' she asked, a warning spark in her eye.

'Just answer them all!'

'Very well. Yes, I'm going to the opera with him, and yes, I know his reputation, and I don't know *who's* going. Satisfied?'

'No, I'm *not* bloody well satisfied! How would you like it if I went out with someone else? If I took his sister out?'

'You mean Phoebe? That wouldn't be quite the same, would it? Phoebe's engaged to be married.'

'*We're* engaged—or near enough.'

'I don't recall ever agreeing to marry you . . . or committing myself to you for life . . . or even agreeing to live with you!'

'So going steady—being as close as we have been for these past months—means nothing to you!'

Her eyelids swept down under his disgruntled gaze. 'Our friendship has meant a lot to me, Andrew,' she assured him, and realised as the words left her lips that she had used the past tense. 'But you don't own me. I'm still a free agent.'

'I thought you loved me!'

'I did—*do*—you're very dear to me, Andrew...as a friend. But not when you're in this mood. Just because a man has invited me to the opera doesn't mean I have plans to jump into his bed!'

'I bet he has plans to jump into yours, given half the chance.' He thrust his face close to hers, his hazel eyes narrowing. 'What are you playing at, Tess? If you wanted to go to the opera so much, why couldn't you have asked me to take you?'

'Because I know the opera bores you to death.'

'And you think he's interested in the opera? It's just an excuse to chase after *you*, Tess...the way he chases after any good-looking woman who catches his eye. Especially a woman he thinks might be harder to get than most. To a man like him, trying to steal you away from me would only be adding a bit of spice. You're a challenge to him, Tess. It'll be flowers next...and intimate dinners for two. He'll use his precious money and his charm to seduce you, the way he uses them to dazzle all the women he chases after. He'd relish a brief fling with you, Tess...just to show everyone how easily he can get any woman he wants! And then he'll drop you like a hot cake, to chase after someone else!'

Tess threw back her head in exasperation, her flaming curls dancing in the glow of the deck's fairy-lights. 'For heaven's sake, Andrew, I'm only going to the *opera* with him! I'm not leaping into his bed!'

'Maybe you'd like to,' Andrew gritted, his face dark.

'I'm not going to stand here and listen to this!' Breaking away from him, she headed for the nearest group of guests—relieved to see there'd been nobody near enough to hear them arguing. 'Thanks for spoiling a pleasant day!' she hissed over her shoulder.

Why was she getting so hot under the collar? Didn't she secretly agree with everything Andrew had said? She was well aware of Piers Branson's rakish reputation. She didn't need any warning from him. But how could she tell Andrew it wasn't Piers Branson she was interested in, but the man who had raised him as his son?

Thankfully, midnight was fast approaching, and the big yacht was already heading back to the Man O' War steps. The other boats on the harbour had thinned out considerably, the twinkling lights of the few remaining dancing on the water, or also moving towards the shore.

Tess tried to maintain a cool, airy demeanour as she and Andrew took their leave of Piers and Phoebe, taking their turn with the other guests to thank their hosts before stepping ashore and heading back to where they'd left their cars.

Piers boldly caught her hand as she added her polite thank-you to Andrew's. 'I'll ring you during the week,' he said easily, making no attempt to lower his voice. As if, Tess thought, they were planning a business meeting rather than a gala night out together! His laughing black eyes, though, lingered on hers in a decidedly *un*businesslike way, causing Phoebe, at his side, to glance from her brother to Andrew. Tess was sure, as Phoebe's gaze then flickered in a faintly puzzled way to *her*, that Piers's sister had noticed Andrew's taut expression and was wondering what Tess and her brother were up to.

In the car on the way home Andrew sat hunched over the wheel in a sullen silence, and

Tess, her own mind filled with thoughts of her own, made no attempt to tease him out of his sulks.

When he pulled up outside her North Sydney flat, she roused herself, giving a deep yawn as she threw open her door.

'Well, that was quite a day! I'm going to sleep like a log. Nothing like a day on the water to —— '

'Aren't you going to invite me in?' Andrew cut in, his voice a low, aggrieved growl.

She paused. 'Not tonight, Andrew. It's late. Do you mind?'

'It's *him*, isn't it? You'd prefer to go to sleep and dream about *him*?'

'Oh, Andrew, you're not going to start all that again! You're being ridiculous!'

'Am I? If you're not interested in him, then why won't you let me come in?'

'I told you—because I'm tired and I want to go to sleep!' She swung her legs out of the car.

He caught her arm. 'Then what about to-morrow night? You will spend tomorrow night with me?'

As she hesitated his hand tightened on her arm. 'Aren't you at least going to kiss me goodnight?'

She twisted round to face him, prepared to comply with a brief kiss before making her escape. But Andrew had other ideas, grabbing her round the waist and jerking her back against him in a rough embrace, his lips clumsily seeking hers.

She squawked a protest as his open mouth clamped down on hers, struggling to free herself as his kisses became more heated, as his fingers began clawing at the scooped neckline of her gold-threaded top, his hand fumbling inside it, grabbing her breast. Managing to wrench her mouth away, she yelped, 'Let me go, damn you!' She tore herself from his grasp and scrambled out of the car, throwing back a snappish, 'Good-*night*, Andrew!' as she stalked off.

Andrew leapt out of the driver's side and ran after her. 'Tess, I'm sorry! I lost my head.' There was a note of panic in his voice now. 'It's just that I... Damn it, I don't want to lose you!'

She halted, swinging round to face him. 'Andrew...I think it might be best,' she said with a sigh, 'if we take a break from each other for a while—it's just not working any more. Oh, it's not just the kiss,' she added quickly as his eyes widened in shock. 'And it's not Piers Branson, or anything that happened today. It's been coming on for some time. I'm just not sure any more. I think we'd better call a halt now.'

'It *is* Piers Branson...why don't you admit it?' Andrew rasped. 'You're just trying to let me down gently. Be honest, Tess! You want me out of the way because you've got your sights set on him now!'

'No!' she denied vehemently. 'I haven't! It's nothing like that!' But how could she tell him the truth—the real reason she wanted to get closer to Piers Branson? She couldn't tell anyone. She wasn't at liberty to tell!

'Isn't it?' His mouth twisted. 'Then why are you giving me the brush-off *now*? Only minutes after Piers Branson invites you out?'

She shook her head, hardly knowing the answer to that herself. Had she really been working up to breaking off with him? And, if she had, why choose now, tonight? Because she needed to concentrate all her energy on the task ahead? On finding out if Julius

Branson really was her father, which was going to mean spending whatever time it took with Piers Branson? Or...was it out of a sense of fair play—to Andrew? Knowing she wouldn't feel right about being involved with two men at the one time?

Not that she intended to get *involved* with Piers Branson, for heaven's sake! Just to get close enough to him to find out more about Julius Branson...and, hopefully, to meet him.

And if that meant playing up to Piers, accepting invitations from him, even flirting with him—to a point—then that was what she was prepared to do. It was only the kind of behaviour that Piers Branson indulged in himself, time and time again, with other women. Toying with them, leading them on, for what he could get in return. Playing him at his own game would be no more than he deserved. It might even teach him a salutary lesson!

'So it is Piers Branson!' Andrew's face darkened. 'Because he can offer you more than I can, I suppose!'

She faced him with raking scorn in her eyes. 'If you don't know me any better than that,

Andrew, then it's just as well we're calling it quits!'

But he was deaf, blind to reason. 'I would never have taken you for the fickle type, Tess. Let alone a gold-digger! My God, I ought to warn him! Warn him you're not to be trusted—that you're only after him for what you can get out of him!'

She flushed, unable to refute the accusation. She *was* after Piers for what she could get out of him. But it wasn't his money—it wasn't the high life or anything *he* could provide. Piers was the key to something far more important to her. To the truth about her origins! She *had* to stay close to him—by any means she knew how.

'You bitch...you can't even deny it!' Andrew reeled away in disgust. 'Well, good luck to you!' he sneered, spitting the words over his shoulder. 'Just don't come crawling back to me when he gives you the flick! Because he *will*!'

CHAPTER THREE

PIERS had told her he would pick her up at seven. At eight minutes past, Tess started tapping her foot. Obviously he wasn't wildly impatient to see her again!

When, a few seconds later, she saw a sleek two-door Jaguar pull into the kerb outside her home unit, and saw Piers's dark head emerge from it, only then did she leave her front porch and step out to meet him. She hadn't wanted to appear over-eager by waiting at the gate. A man like Piers Branson, she suspected, would soon grow weary of a woman who was too easily attainable. And she didn't want him tiring of her, and ditching her, just yet!

'Ah, you're ready,' were the first words he said, in an almost surprised tone, as he strode forward to meet her. She felt her throat constrict at the sight of him in his black dinner-jacket, his shirt snowy white against his black bow tie, an easy elegance in his loose-limbed stride. His dark hair was neatly slicked down

52

rather than wind-blown as it had been the other day, and a wicked eyebrow quirked in that faintly mocking way of his. Even now, neatly groomed as he was, she noted that a few stray hairs were spraying over his tanned brow. Ridiculously, it made her fingers itch to reach out and stroke the wayward strands.

She swallowed hard, and murmured, 'You weren't expecting me to be?' as he caught her hand and pressed it lightly, sending hot prickles up her arm.

'I always give a woman a few extra minutes.' His dark eyes danced as they met hers. 'I invariably find they need it.'

So much for his opinion of women, she thought. It said a lot about the kind of women he normally escorted!

'Not me,' she said crisply, slipping her hand from his as they walked to his car. 'I wouldn't want to risk arriving late at the Opera House and missing the first act.'

'You mean you're only concerned about missing the performance? You don't care if you miss out on the socialising in the foyer beforehand . . . with the glitterati?' he asked, his eyes teasing.

'Is that what *you'd* miss?' she asked with a twinge of disappointment. Was he no different from Andrew?

'We're talking about you, Tess, not me,' he said as he opened his passenger door with a flourish, waiting until she was settled in her seat before stepping round to the driver's side. 'I'm glad you didn't get too dolled up,' he said approvingly as he slid in beside her. 'Some women go overboard at these gala nights.'

The women he normally took out, no doubt!

'I'm glad you approve,' she said drily.

'I more than approve—you look stunning, Tess. Few women realise that simplicity and elegance have far more knockout appeal than all that glitzy, over-the-top high-fashion gear... and masses of gaudy jewellery. Or endless gold chains and bangles that jangle all through a performance.'

Tess smiled, relieved that he approved of her choice. She had been afraid he might think that her simple basic black, with its neat cap sleeves and high square neckline, wasn't dressy enough. She'd tried dressing it up with jewellery, experimenting with some of her modest gold and silver pieces, but they'd looked cheap and garish—or she knew they *would*, beside the real thing. She'd opted instead for the simple cameo brooch that her mother had given her for her graduation, with matching ear-rings.

'It's too hot at this time of year to weigh yourself down with a lot of jewellery and glitz,' she said with a brief shrug. 'This is Sydney, not London or Milan. People don't expect you to go overboard here. Especially in midsummer.' Even on gala charity nights, she hoped.

'You'd shine anywhere, Tess . . . just as you are,' he said gallantly. 'You don't need to wear jewellery or glitzy high fashion to stand out. Your hair is adornment enough—it's like a dazzling crown. A perfect frame for a perfect face. And with that tall, regal bearing of yours . . . and those legs . . .' He gave a low whistle. 'You don't need any dolling up, Tess.'

Oh, please, she thought, her lip twisting in disbelief at his over-the-top compliments—even as she was conscious of a tiny zing of exhilaration.

Somehow she managed to respond in a light, bubbly tone. 'Much more of this flattery, Piers, and you'll be turning my head.' Did he think he *had* to flatter her? Was that what his women normally expected of him? And why, for heaven's sake, was she reacting to it? Because it gave her a sense of satisfaction? After all, she'd *wanted* to attract him, hadn't she?

'As long as it turns my way,' Piers returned, 'I won't mind.'

She deliberately looked away from him at that, gazing out of the car window at nothing in particular.

'Not that the right piece of jewellery wouldn't suit you,' Piers said slowly, and she felt him slide an appraising look round at her, even while he kept his attention on the traffic ahead. 'A simple diamond necklace worn with that dress...wow! You'd knock everyone's eyes out.'

She drew in a long breath. She had the oddest feeling that he was fishing ... probing ... trying to find out if she really did secretly covet fine jewellery. The real thing. Diamonds. He must know she couldn't afford them herself. Her medical practice was doing well, but not that well. It had cost an arm and a leg to start up her own practice, something she could never have done without the help of her unknown benefactor. Her father.

He's trying to *bribe* me! she realised, her lips tightening. Give me a good time, Tess, and I'll reward you handsomely.

His gaze was intent now on the traffic converging on the Opera House, but she had the feeling that his mind was not, that all his senses were alive and waiting. Waiting for her to make the admission he expected. After all, weren't diamonds supposed to be a girl's best friend? And everyone knew the Bransons were one family wealthy enough to buy them!

She hissed out her breath. 'A second ago,' she said tartly, 'you said I looked stunning *without* any showy jewellery! And I'm not fishing for more compliments!' she said quickly. 'Can't we talk about something else? How is your father?' she asked.

He glanced round at her then, his eyes narrowing, an enigmatic look in the black depths, before they flicked back to the road. 'He's bouncing back. He'll be leaving hospital in the morning...against all advice, of course. But he insists on going home.'

So... he would be home tomorrow, convalescing. Piers, no doubt, would visit him there. If Piers wanted to see more of her, he might, just might, take her with him on one of his visits to see his father!

'Your parents live on the harbour somewhere, don't they?' she asked lightly.

'Point Piper. But he won't be going there —— ' Piers broke off as he swung the car into the Opera House car park. She was dying to ask where his father *would* be going, her heart sinking at the thought of him leaving Sydney. But she'd only make him suspicious if she started asking questions now. Besides, he had other things on his mind right now. Like finding a parking spot.

'Well, how did you enjoy it?' Piers asked as they rose from their plush seats. Centre front row of the dress circle—nothing but the best for the Bransons!

She turned to him with a smile. 'It was wonderful! The music, the singing, the sets, everything! And that glorious aria in the Third Act—the duet between Antonia and Dr Miracle—it was simply sublime. It always brings tears to my eyes... and gives me goosebumps all over.' Her enthusiasm added sparkle to the deep blue of her eyes. 'Did *you* enjoy it?'

He seemed faintly surprised at the question, that it would even occur to her to ask. As if he'd brought her here to please and impress *her*, and his own pleasure was by the by.

'Very much,' he said, his smiling black eyes gazing deeply—too deeply—into hers.

She glanced away. He wanted her to think he'd only enjoyed it because of her, but she knew that wasn't true. He had genuinely enjoyed it—she had sensed it throughout the stunning performance. He had been as absorbed, as transported, as she had.

'I thought you must have,' she said lightly. 'I noticed you didn't go to sleep.'

'Is that what Andrew usually does? Goes to sleep?'

Wishing he hadn't reminded her of Andrew, she merely smiled. She still felt guilty about breaking off with Andrew so abruptly. She ought to have gone about it more gently...and picked a different time to do it. She had damaged his pride—never mind his heart— by choosing the very day she had met Piers Branson and agreed to go out with him. But it was a bit late to worry about it now. Andrew couldn't have been too shattered. She hadn't seen or heard from him since.

'I saw him a couple of days ago,' Piers remarked as they filed out, behind his sister Phoebe and her fiancé Tom, who had been sitting with them.

She asked quickly, 'To speak to?'

'Sure. We bumped into each other at the lawcourts.'

She looked up at him inquiringly, dying to ask what they'd said, and if the meeting had been amicable. If Andrew had still been in the mood he'd been in when she last saw him, the two could have come to blows! At the very least, Andrew could have carried out his threat to warn Piers against her. She bit her lip. She couldn't ask here—there were too many people within hearing. Many of them knew Piers, a few calling out to him, wanting to know what he'd thought of the performance. Giving her speculative looks at the same time, the way they had in the foyer during the intervals.

One man, sidling up to Piers on their way out, went so far as to chide him jokingly, 'We don't often see you at these gala nights, Piers.

I think you only attend them when you want to show off your latest beautiful lady-friend!' Winking at Tess, he added crassly—maybe to warn her— 'Always a different girl, you devil...and each one more stunning than the last. One finds it hard to keep track!'

Piers muttered something under his breath as the man moved away, and Tess laughed and said, 'The truth hurts, Piers?' even as a distinct uneasiness tugged at her insides. Had Piers only invited her out tonight as a one-off thing...to give her a glittering night out to enjoy and remember? After all, as far as he knew, Andrew was still in the picture. Maybe he had rules of morality and decency after all. Maybe he thought she'd only agreed to let him escort her tonight because she was keen on the opera and Andrew wasn't—and because, like most of the women he knew, she was ready to jump at the chance to attend such a dazzling event.

Damn, she thought, seeing her chances of meeting Julius Branson dissolving with the night.

Somehow she would have to let him know that she'd broken off with Andrew. It would be tricky. She didn't want Piers thinking it was because of him—that she was chasing him. A girl needed to play hard to get to hold the interest of a man like Piers Branson.

She had almost forgotten the teasing question she had asked until Piers surprised her by answering, 'I was thinking of *your* feelings, Tess. The insensitive fool!'

Her eyes leapt to his. His black eyes were warm and soft as they met and searched her own. She felt quite dizzy under the darkly mesmerising gaze. This man sure knows how to charm a woman, she thought unsteadily. Piers had the kind of charm that could make a woman feel she was the only person in the world who existed, who mattered to him. At least, in that moment. The trouble was...men with charm like that could fool a dozen women into thinking they were the only one!

'Always a different girl,' that man had said.

She gathered her wits to retort lightly, with a hint of challenge in her eyes, 'Well, forewarned is forearmed, so they say. Tomorrow, no doubt, it will be another woman on your arm!'

'I doubt that very much,' Piers returned softly, and she glanced away with a disbelieving toss of her head, aware of a tiny flutter of elation.

Ten minutes into the supper overlooking the twinkling lights of Sydney Harbour, Piers whispered, 'Let's leave this bunfight and find a quiet place for a light snack on our own.'

She flicked a tongue over her lips. 'Suits me.'

'You're sure you don't mind leaving?' he asked as he caught her arm and began guiding her through the glittering throng. The cream of Sydney society had gathered in force.

'Not a bit.' Standing around making polite conversation with people she didn't know, even though she recognised many a well-known name and face, including the Prime Minister himself and the State Premier, was not her cup of tea. Especially trying to talk intelligently over the din, and nibble the offered delicacies and hold on to a champagne glass, all at the same time—to say nothing of being jostled by elbows and people pushing past, eager to dive on someone they knew. Most were dressed to kill. Or dressed to *compete*, she thought wryly. It was a relief to know that Piers felt the same. Andrew, if he were here, would be lapping it up, dashing from group to group, making sure everybody knew he was there.

Of course, Piers's motivation for leaving early might be far more basic than simply avoiding a VIP bunfight. Like getting her on her own...for *purposes* of his own!

'Sneaking out already, Piers?' a voice enquired as they neared the exit. Glancing round, Tess recognised the face of a well-known Sydney entrepreneur. 'Not that I blame you.' The man's bespectacled gaze roved admiringly over her. 'You've really hit the jackpot this time—half your luck!'

'Could be,' Piers drawled, barely pausing. 'Forgive us...' His smile flashed an apology. 'We're running late for another engagement.'

He shot up a hand as a photographer raised his camera. 'No photographs!' he snapped as they swept past.

Tess realised, as they reached the stairs, that they hadn't even said farewell to Phoebe and Tom, who'd been lost somewhere in the crush. But no doubt Phoebe was used to her brother racing off with his latest female companion!

'Well, where shall we go?' Piers asked as he nosed his slinky Jaguar out of the car park. 'A nightclub?'

Tess's spirits nosedived. But if that was the only way to hold Piers' interest... 'If you want to,' she said, repressing a shudder. All those flashing lights, the ear-shattering music, the smoke... She couldn't think of anything worse. She wanted to go somewhere where she could talk to Piers—and how could they talk in a place like that? Maybe he didn't *want* to talk. Maybe he just wanted to writhe and shuffle to the music, and have a few more drinks, until he had her in the mood to...

She felt her mouth go dry.

'You don't sound too enthused,' Piers commented. 'I thought women loved going to nightclubs.'

Not this woman, Piers. Only the types who chase after you, I imagine. She stifled a sigh. This was useless—it was never going to work. Playing up to Piers Branson, pretending to be someone she wasn't, deliberately using her feminine wiles, using *Piers* to get to his father. It was all wrong. She was making a big mistake.

'If that sigh means what I think it means,' Piers murmured, 'I'm with you. Nightclubs can be a dead bore. You can't hear yourself think, let alone speak. How about we go back to your place?' he suggested. 'You can make me some coffee.'

Her heart missed a beat. Was it only coffee he wanted? Only to talk? Or did he have something more...cosy in mind? She ran a nervous tongue over her dry lips. Was he the type to expect a special kind of thank-you in return for a gala night out?

'I'm afraid I don't have any fresh coffee at home,' she demurred. 'Maybe we could find a coffee-bar...or a nice café somewhere...'

His eyebrow shot up. 'Instant will do. I'm not fussy. And I'm sure your chairs at home are more comfy than any we'd find in any café. *And* more conducive to a leisurely chat.'

She eyed him narrowly as he swung the car round. He was already heading for the Harbour Bridge. For North Sydney!

'Well...OK,' she heard herself concurring. 'As long as you're willing to settle for instant coffee...and a friendly chat,' she added, spelling it out.

His mouth curved in a thoroughly charming, thoroughly irrepressible grin. 'Message received, Doctor.'

She smiled back, her tense muscles easing, even as she wondered if she was being naïve—mad to trust him. With his kind of wealth and background, Piers Branson must be used to getting whatever he wanted... whenever he wanted it. He was probably used to women putting up a token resistance, so as not to appear too easy, and imagined that she was playing a similar game. Well, he'd find out! But first... Well, at least she would have a chance to talk to him now... and to ask a few questions.

'Don't expect anything fancy,' she warned him, adding drily, 'It's not the kind of palace you must be used to.'

The black eyes leapt round, bright with amusement. 'What makes you think I live in a palace?'

'Well, don't you?' She assumed a bantering tone. 'I've heard about how the Bransons live—their palatial home on the harbour, their luxury apartments around the world, their vast property up north, their own private tropical island...'

His eyebrow rose. 'Sounds good to you, does it?'

She was about too flatten him with a tart retort, when she remembered that she wanted to meet Julius Branson. 'Well...it doesn't sound hard to take,' she said coolly.

He pursed his lips, lifting his shoulders and letting them fall. 'You can only sit in one chair at a time. You can only eat at one table at a time. Or lie in one bed at a time. My needs are simpler than you think.'

She squinted at him. Had he mentioned beds deliberately?

'Well, I'm glad to hear it,' she said lightly. 'We'll put it to the test when we get to my place.'

His grin flashed again. 'You mean the chair...or the bed?'

She flushed. 'Very definitely, the *chair*,' she said crushingly, glad of the chance to make it clear. Let him stew on that, she thought. If he doesn't like it, he can drop me off at my door and not come in.

Two seconds later, when he'd made no comment, she found her teeth tugging at her lip. Maybe he *was* stewing it over. Maybe he'd decided not to come in after all, to cut his losses and run. For good! No! her mind rebelled. He can't! I need him!

She lapsed into a deep silence of her own, planning what strategy she would use to make him change his mind...just in case she needed it.

When he pulled up outside her home unit—the front one of a block of four—she held her breath. Held it right up until he'd walked her to her front door and followed her inside, only then releasing it. She felt her heart jumping with relief. And something else. Expectancy. Anticipation. A heady excitement.

Nothing personal, she was quick to assure herself. It was just the challenge of knowing that it was now up to her. It was up to her to spark his interest enough so that he'd want to see her again, after tonight.

'Very nice,' he said as he looked around. The unit was brand new, with an open, spacious feel about it, though her mixture of old and new furniture cluttered it up somewhat. She was glad she'd thought to tidy the place up earlier, before he came to pick her up. Just in case he'd been early and had wanted to come in. Early! He'd been nearly ten minutes late. Expecting her to be even later!

She sucked in her lips. Maybe that was the way to keep his interest alive. By surprising him—by doing the opposite to what he was expecting, the opposite to what his other women friends would do.

She caught him glancing through the open door of her bedroom at her doona-covered bed, and said quickly, wishing as she said it that her heart would settle down to a more normal beat, 'You're in luck. I've just re-membered ... I stored some ground coffee in my freezer. So you won't have to settle for instant, after all. Back in a minute,' she said a trifle breathlessly, making a dive for the kitchen. 'Make yourself comfortable!' she flung over her shoulder.

'I'll come and watch.' His voice, close behind her, made the hairs at her nape spring up in response. She tried not to fumble as she put the water on to boil and extracted the pack of coffee from the freezer, vividly conscious of his eyes on her as she reached up for coffee-mugs and a bowl, and tipped a handful of chocolate-coated mints from a packet into the bowl.

'How long have you been here?' he asked, and when she glanced round she saw him leaning on her ceramic-tiled island bench with his firm jaws resting on his hands. He was still watching her, the wicked black eyes partially veiled by his thick black lashes.

'Only a few months,' she said, turning away in some relief as the water began to boil. 'I was living with my mother before that. Not all the time, of course—I've had to move around between one hospital and another for years. But I moved back in with her for a while after I started up my practice. To save money.'

'And you left home again when you met Andrew?'

She flushed at the mention of Andrew's name, and shook her head, her back still turned to him. 'I was already seeing Andrew. No... I left home because my mother died.' She kept her face averted, pressing down the coffee-plunger as she spoke. 'I decided to sell the house and buy a home unit, closer to my practice.'

She jumped as she felt his hand on her shoulder. She hadn't even heard him coming!

'I'm sorry about your mother, Tess. Was it a long illness?'

'Not exactly—it was very sudden, in the end.' She poured the coffee, then picked up the two mugs, while Piers, without being asked, reached for the plate of mints. 'She'd suffered for years with rheumatoid arthritis,' she told him as she led him back to the living-room. 'But it got particularly bad about a year ago. She would have been confined to a wheelchair before long if she...' She faltered, swallowing. The memory was still painful. 'She had a massive heart attack. It was very sudden. I wasn't home at the time and the nurse who came in during the day wasn't able to save her.'

'That's tough.' His sympathy seemed genuine.

'My mother would have wanted it that way,' Tess said painfully. 'She would have hated life in a wheelchair. And she'd been in terrible pain in the months leading up to her... To the attack.'

Piers hovered over her as she set the mugs down on a low table. 'Now I understand why you chose to become a rheumatologist,' he said, his voice soft, soothing. 'You wanted to stop others suffering the way your mother suffered.'

'Something like that,' she said. She waved him to her deepest, most comfortable armchair. 'Sit there,' she invited. 'It's not the greatest chair in the world, but I'll bet you've never sat in more comfort.'

He sank into it. 'Mmm...you're right. I may not ever want to get up.'

Good, she thought, feeling a little safer. She chose a more upright armchair for herself and sat down, realising as she crossed her legs that his eyes were on them. She saw faint beads of sweat on his upper lip as he ran his gaze down the length of her long, stockinged legs, down to her slim ankles and then up again, caressing her slender knees and the smooth curve of her thigh before lingering at the spot where her leg vanished under the black hem of her dress.

She felt a wave of heat sweep up her throat into her cheeks. So much for feeling safe!

'It's just as well you're not a heart surgeon, Tess,' Piers said, his voice sounding thicker than usual, lacking its usual banter.

'A *heart* surgeon?' she echoed, staring at him.

'In that sexy dress—and with legs like yours—you'd have an endless stream of poor guys lining up for urgent heart surgery. You'd never have a free moment!'

She laughed—a low, husky sound. 'My patients don't normally see me dressed like this.' Few people did, she reflected. Normally—certainly during the day—she wore clothes that concealed whatever charms she possessed, wanting to hide her long legs and minimise her height, not show them off. It was a habit she'd fallen into during her student days, and her days as a young intern. Wanting to be taken seriously. Not wanting to put up with the sexist comments and advances of her male colleagues and patients.

'You only dress like this for people like me . . . or Andrew?' Piers asked silkily.

Men, he meant. She hid a grimace. How could she blame him for thinking it? Hadn't she gone out of her way, since she'd known him, to be noticed? To catch and hold *his* interest, in particular? First on the boat. And now tonight.

She seized on Andrew's name as a diversion. 'You say you saw Andrew the other day. How . . . was he?'

'Did he mention *you*, you mean?' Piers's black eyes mocked her. 'Oh, yes...he had quite a bit to say, Tess. About you.'

She met the taunting eyes with an effort, determined not to drop her own gaze or show any sign of guilt or apprehension. Had Andrew carried out his threat to warn Piers against her? Had he been openly hostile towards Piers? She waited, willing Piers to tell her.

When he didn't say anything, she admitted with a sigh, 'He wasn't very happy the last time I saw him.'

'No... He didn't seem too happy when I saw him,' Piers agreed. He gave her a quizzical look. 'I take it you haven't seen him since Australia Day?'

Tess swallowed. Damn, damn, damn, she thought. Now that he knows that, he'll be convinced I broke up with Andrew because of *him*. Giving weight to what Andrew had no doubt told him about her. As he had threatened to tell him. That she had her sights set a lot higher than a lowly corporate lawyer!

She broke eye contact at last, to reach for her coffee. How could she tell Piers that Andrew, not she, was the one whose sights were set on bigger and better things: on impressing people who counted, on achieving more and more money and success? She couldn't say a word—not without throwing Piers's wealth and cushy lifestyle back in his face, and blowing any chance of getting to meet Julius Branson. If Piers wanted to believe he had something to offer her that she wanted, then let him believe it. For now. It could lead to a meeting with the father she had never known. And that was *all* she wanted.

'So...you *have* broken off with him?' Piers drawled. The black eyes were hooded and unreadable as she glanced back at him. She couldn't tell if he was elated about it, or uneasy. She felt like kicking herself for being so stupid as to break off with Andrew at this point. If she'd kept him dangling, as other women would have done, she suspected—regardless of scruples—it might have made Piers even more determined to pursue her. Rich, pampered playboys had few morals, she'd be prepared to bet, when it came to stealing women away from other men!

'Do you mind if we don't talk about Andrew?' she begged. Let him think what he pleased. Let him think she was as ruthless as he was. Just as long as he wanted to see her again!

CHAPTER FOUR

'AND your father?' Piers asked, bowing to her wish not to talk about Andrew.

She tensed. 'My father?'

'Is your father still alive?'

Gulping, Tess answered as calmly as she could, 'I never knew my father.'

'You mean they split up before you were born? They...never married?'

Tess took a deep breath, knowing she would have to be very careful how she answered. 'My mother *was* married,' she began cautiously. 'Her husband—the man I grew up believing was my father, even though my mother always denied it—walked out on her before I was born. He didn't want children, according to my mother. He'd told her that if she ever got pregnant he'd leave her. Because she loved him so much and didn't want to lose him she agreed...in the beginning. But when she found out that she was pregnant and her husband told her to have an abortion, she refused. And so...he left her. They divorced, and my mother never saw him again. Never wanted to. She reverted to her maiden name and wouldn't even talk about him.'

'The swine.' Piers toyed with the coffee-cup in his hands. 'You said you grew up *believing* he was your father. You don't any more?'

Tess shook her head, taking a long sip of her coffee before answering. 'After my mother died I went in search of him. I'm not sure why. I just needed to know, I guess. I thought my mother had only denied he was my father because of the way he'd hurt her. She always swore he wasn't, but she would never tell me who it *was*—she said she couldn't. She died without telling me.' Tess blinked a prickle of moisture from her eyes.

She had deliberately made no mention of the money that had been paid into her mother's bank account twice a year since her birth, and was still coming, being paid now into her own account. It would be dicing with danger to mention that! Piers dabbled in the law and must know lots of lawyers. He just might know her mother's lawyers, and try to worm the truth out of them, thinking he was doing her a good turn. She shuddered at the thought of him finding out the truth and openly confronting Julius—maybe in front of his mother Delia. Or turning on *her*, Tess, for the way she had deceived him, used him. She wanted to find out the truth quietly, in private—to keep it between Julius and herself, not have it brought out into the open and shouted to the world. She knew it would only lead to the people closest to Julius—his wife and family—getting hurt. All she wanted was to know the truth of her origins, for her own peace of mind.

'And did you manage to track him down?' Piers asked. 'Your mother's ex-husband?'

Tess examined the pattern on the mug in her hands. 'Eventually. He confirmed what my mother had told me. I wasn't his daughter.'

'And you believed him?'

She nodded, glancing up again, surprised at the compassion she heard in his voice, the understanding she glimpsed in the black eyes that normally held only a wicked amusement. She wouldn't have thought him capable of feelings of that nature—of sympathy and understanding of another person's feelings. People talked of the fun-loving playboy...playing with life, playing with women, playing with the law, intent only on his own hedonistic pleasures. But maybe there was more to him.

He'd make a good barrister, she mused, the way he probes, and draws out answers. What a pity he's going to give it all up one day to take control of his father's media empire. Waste of a good talent!

'What made you believe him?' Piers pressed.

She shrugged. 'I knew the moment I laid eyes on him. I looked nothing like him. I didn't take after my mother, either, you see— she was fair, with grey eyes. He was dark-eyed and dark-haired. He said he'd never wanted a child of his own and he was damned if he was going to bring up another man's child. That was why he'd left my mother, he told me. He's married to someone else now,' she added with a rueful tilt of her lips. 'And they're happy, he took pains to assure me. *Childless* and happy.'

'Was he able to tell you who your father was?' Piers asked, his voice velvet-soft, as attractive as it was compelling.

Tess swallowed, and shook her head. 'He said my mother had refused to tell him. Just as she'd always refused to tell me.' Her eyelids fluttered down, shuttering her eyes. She had no intention of telling Piers Branson what else her mother's ex-husband had told her. That, according to Tess's mother, the man who had made her pregnant was a happily married man, whose identity he had insisted she keep a secret. 'But it wasn't hard,' Michael Lawrence had told Tess with a twisted smile, 'to guess who it was.'

At her urging, he had opened up further. 'She was working at the time as private secretary to a wealthy businessman—a married man who's since soared to the top of the Australian business world and made a fortune. They worked very closely together. They even went away together... ostensibly on business.' His lip had curled at that. 'She came back pregnant from one of their business trips together. As far as I know, she was never close to anyone else. I've no proof, mind,' he'd added hastily. 'Don't quote me,' he warned. 'I work for one of his newspapers, and I don't want to lose my job.'

Tess had demanded to know the man's name. When he had told her it was Julius Branson, she had been speechless. One of the richest, most powerful men in Australia, her *father*? It seemed impossible—putting him far out of her reach. She hadn't known what to do, how to get close enough to him to find out the truth...until Andrew had received his Australia Day invitation.

'Your father's name was never on your birth certificate?' Piers's voice broke into her thoughts.

'No.' She scrutinised the dregs in the bottom of her coffee-mug, wanting to hide the flare of apprehension in her eyes. Had she told Piers too much? She didn't want him using his famous name or his legal connections to delve on her behalf. It could be disastrous. For all of them!

'You're a natural redhead, Tess?'

'Pardon?' Her head shot up. Suddenly she felt sick. What if Julius Branson was a vivid redhead too, and a possible connection had just struck Piers? She had seen the odd newspaper photograph of the media tycoon, but never one in colour, and not recently. From memory, his hair had been light in colour. But it had been hard to tell. Pale ginger, perhaps?

She chided herself for being a fool. Piers had no reason to connect his father with her.

None. She was getting jumpy for no reason. She was just thankful she hadn't mentioned to him that her mother had once worked for Julius Branson!

She forced a rueful smile. 'Yes...worse luck. Can't you tell?' She extended a pale arm. 'I'd love to have skin that tanned easily. To be able to lie out in the sun all day long.'

'Most girls would kill to have that clear, translucent skin of yours,' Piers said promptly. 'And that hair...' His eyes seared over it in a way that would have made most things, she mused breathlessly, spontaneously combust under their heat. 'It's the most glorious colour I've ever seen. If you take after your father,' he added reflectively, 'it should narrow the field considerably. There can't be too many people around with hair like yours.'

She felt hot prickles break out on her skin. 'You'd be surprised,' she said evasively. Change the subject, you fool.

'I've talked enough about myself,' she said briskly, avoiding his gaze as she put down her empty mug. 'Tell me something about yourself, Piers,' she invited, striving to keep her tone light. 'Your own upbringing. Your family. Your parents.' Tell me about Julius Branson, was what she really wanted to ask.

Piers's black eyes appeared to be searching her face as she glanced back at him. If only she knew what he was searching *for*, what he was thinking! Surely he didn't suspect anything? He couldn't!

'I barely remember my parents,' he said after a moment, and she realised after a startled second that he was talking about his real parents, not the Bransons. 'They were close friends of the Bransons and, after they were killed in an overseas accident, Phoebe and I were legally adopted by the Bransons, who brought us up as their own children. Jules and Dee weren't able to have children of their own.'

'You must be very grateful to them,' Tess said, wanting to bring the conversation back to Julius Branson. Wanting to know all she could about him. 'People say you're a close-knit family—is that true?' she asked, adopting an air of natural curiosity.

Piers surveyed her from under a raised eyebrow. 'I guess we're not much different from most families.'

She laughed disbelievingly. 'Most families don't have a string of houses, a luxury motor-yacht, a private island, a cattle-station the size of France...' If she enthused enough, maybe Piers would invite her into his private family world...and she would be able to meet Julius.

'Are those the things *you'd* like, Tess?' Piers asked softly.

Just in time, she bit back the, Heavens, no! on her lips. Instead, she ran her tongue over her lips and said, 'I wouldn't know. I've never known those things.' She spoke lightly, flippantly, as if she didn't expect to know them either...but secretly hoping that, if Piers was at all interested in her, he might decide to show at least some of them to her. Preferably, wherever Julius Branson had gone to recuperate!

He was watching her. His eyes were fixed to her mouth, as if mesmerised by the moisture her tongue had left on them.

She swallowed, and glanced at her watch. 'Forgive me...but it's getting awfully late.'

'You're right.' Piers hauled himself, with some difficulty, from his deep armchair. She rose too, and found herself stepping back nervously as he took a step, not towards the door, but towards her. She was brought to a halt when the backs of her legs touched the arm-chair behind her.

In sudden panic, she tried to twist away, mumbling as she swung round, 'It's been a wonderful night, Piers. Just wonderful. I— I'll see you to the door.'

'Hey...not so fast!' A hand caught her by the shoulder, swinging her round to face him.

She paused, looking up at him helplessly. Oh, hell, she thought in swift self-derision, despising the weakness that had suddenly turned her limbs to rubber. This is a first the cool-hearted Dr Keneally feeling helpless in the arms of a man!

She summoned all her will-power to bring back that vanished coolness. 'We agreed— just coffee and a chat!' It came out more a croak then a cool reminder.

'Just one kiss, Tess—a goodnight kiss, in return for your "wonderful night"?' he pleaded. His voice was husky, his eyes like black fire, compelling in their intensity, weak-ening her further. 'I've been wanting to kiss those luscious lips of yours from the moment I first set eyes on you!'

She shook her head in swift rejection, though her whole body was trembling in treacherous anticipation. She too wanted nothing more than to feel his lips on hers, she realised, but she was afraid that one kiss might lead to another, and another, and heaven knew what might happen after that. And then, having got what he'd set out to get—yet another easy conquest under his belt—it would be exit, Piers Branson. Blowing her best chance—maybe her only chance—of meeting Julius Branson.

'I never kiss on a first date!' she gasped, her body quivering as his musky male scent tantalised her nostrils.

His eyebrow shot up. 'I thought that was: never go to bed on a first date?'

'It could be the same thing...to some people!'

'Not to me, Tess...I promise. Just a kiss.'

Her tongue darted across her lips. 'OK...but not here,' she said, seeing a way out—while still getting a taste of what her lips were longing for. 'On the front porch. Just a goodnight kiss, you said!'

His black eyes glittered. 'You're a hard woman, Tess. But if that's the only way I'll get my kiss...'

'That's the one and only way!' She broke free and spun away, lunging for the door. 'Take it or leave it!' she flung over her shoulder, gaining courage now that she was out of his arms.

But moments later she was back in them, and it was even more intimate, even more intoxicating, out here on her tiny porch, with the balmy night air caressing them and the velvety blackness above, sprinkled with a myriad tiny stars and a silvery crescent moon. And the arms round her were far, far too tempting.

This is wrong, she thought with a renewed flare of conscience, her lips trembling as she raised her face to his. It's wrong to lead him on like this. But how would she ever find out the truth about her father if she didn't use Piers to bring her within reach of Julius Branson? It's only a simple kiss he wants, she reasoned, her breath fluttering in her throat. What's wrong with a kiss?

But she wasn't prepared for the shock his kiss brought, the first touch of his lips on hers sending spirals of heat spinning down her body, fizzing along her limbs. Dazedly, her mind registered the sensuous feel and warmth of his mouth, the heady taste of his lips— light, testing kisses at first, growing gradually deeper, more passionate. His hand was moving over her back, his fingers sliding up her nape into her tumbled curls. She heard sighing sounds coming from his throat...or were they coming from her own?

Despite herself, she felt her lips flowering under the increasing pressure of his. Of their own volition her arms had somehow curled themselves round his neck, and her fingers were brushing over his skin, splaying out over the soft thickness of his hair.

'I knew,' he breathed against her lips, 'that it was going to be good for us, Tess. Our lips were made for each other...'

His voice, his words, reminded her, with a stir of unease, that this was Piers Branson— playboy and practised lover. They had to be words he'd used a thousand times before, to heaven knew how many women before her! She ought to laugh at them, mock them... Why couldn't she seem to? Why didn't she *want* to? Because, stupidly, impossibly, that was how she felt too? His lips on hers felt so *right*.

His hands were skimming down her body now, over her slender curves. She could feel her nerve-ends responding to his touch, a hot sweetness spreading deep inside her body. She knew she ought to be protesting, breaking away from him here and now, but a strange lethargy had invaded her limbs. And a piercing curiosity, an urge to feel more of these delicious sensations. They were more thrilling, more intense than any she'd ever had before, even with Andrew. Wanting to feel more, to find out more, she melted against his warm, sinewy strength.

His response was immediate, his tongue flicking between her lips, ravishing her mouth, his heartbeat quickening against her own. But when she felt his hand roving intimately over the swell of her breast she stiffened and, with a muffled gasp, drew back, her arms sliding from his shoulders, reluctantly escaping the silken web he was weaving around her.

A sense of shame swept over her. This is wrong! she thought again, stepping back away from him. Encouraging him. Using him. Using her body to get what she wanted from him. Never mind if he was using her too, if he was only after her for *her* body, for some easy, meaningless gratification! She wasn't prepared to be so cold-blooded—though he would probably see it as being worldly and sophisticated. Obviously she wasn't as worldly and sophisticated as he thought, as *she'd* foolishly thought. All those years of studying, of working long hours, had left her with little time to play around...and with little experience, despite her medical knowledge, despite her age, despite her time with Andrew.

'Don't tell me you didn't like that too, Tess...and want more of it?' Piers challenged softly as she twisted away from him.

She shook her head. 'Just a kiss, you said!' she upbraided him, not daring to answer his question...even to herself. There must be no more of this, she decided, ignoring the faint tremors that still shook her body. She was prepared to use her wits and her wiles, and even her looks, to get a meeting with Julius Branson, but she didn't intend to use her body as well...much as it might be willing her to! She would be no better than—than a vamp! A Mata Hari!

Some Mata Hari! For a few seconds she had fallen into her own trap, and felt things she hadn't expected to feel, things she'd never felt before. A few seconds more and she could have been in very real danger of throwing discretion to the winds and losing all control. A scary feeling. No... Obviously these sophisticated little games were not for her!

'Come sailing with me tomorrow,' Piers urged, standing away from her, making no attempt to draw her back into his arms.

She caught her breath. So he did want to see her again!

'I... Won't you want to go and see your father?' she asked, bringing his mind back to Julius. She had to get that meeting with Julius Branson. And quickly, before things got out of hand!

Her heart fluttered at the thought. They mustn't *get* out of hand! If Julius Branson should in fact, by some miracle, turn out to be her father, and he acknowledged it, then Piers Branson would be...her half-brother, in the eyes of the law, if not by actual ties of the blood, Julius having legally adopted him.

Piers was eyeing her speculatively, his eyes black pools in the dimness. 'Your concern for my father is touching,' he drawled, his lip lifting in wry amusement. 'It was only a gall-bladder operation.'

'Any operation is serious,' Tess said, adopting the brisk tone she used as a doctor. 'You're not close to your father?' she challenged him.

'On the contrary, I plan to fly up to visit him next weekend. He's going up to Akama to recuperate—our island in the Whitsundays. The house is always open—my Aunt Camille, who's terminally ill, lives there permanently.'

Next weekend—a whole week away! Tess drew in a long, considering breath. Could she hold Piers's interest until then? Fight him off until then? And yet at the same time keep him interested enough to make him want to take her up to the Whitsundays with him? Would he?

'You're not going up this weekend? Tomorrow?' she asked hopefully, feigning a simple curiosity. 'Your father's not feeling up to having visitors or family around him just yet?'

Piers's eyebrow rose a fraction higher and she felt an uneasy flutter. Was he wondering why she was showing so much interest in Julius Branson?

'I visited him in hospital today,' he said with a shrug. 'I'm sure he'll survive without seeing me for another week. Phoebe and Tom are flying up this weekend, as a matter of fact. We don't want to swamp Jules with kindness and good will! Besides, I'm in the middle of a major court case at the moment. I have to stay in town.'

A major court case... He made it sound important. Just how important *was* his law career to him? Tess wondered sceptically, remembering what Andrew had said about him only playing at the law. Was he just using it as an excuse to stay in town...so that he could go on pursuing *her*?

'Well?' Piers's voice dropped to a persuasive purr. 'Will you come sailing with me tomorrow?'

'I'm sorry...I can't. I'm working,' she said, remembering the story she'd told him earlier. The court case sure must be important to him, she thought derisively, if he can spend his weekend sailing!

'Then what about dinner tomorrow night?'

Her eyes wavered as she visualised another night fighting off his advances. A day out sailing would have been far safer! Then she could have begged off in the evening, pleading exhaustion—or sunstroke!

She shook her head. 'I...promised to go to the theatre with a friend.'

'Andrew?' The question rapped out.

'A *girl*-friend,' she said, hating herself for lying. Was she being a damn fool, playing so hard to get? Was she risking him losing interest in her altogether?

'Put her off!'

She gaped at him. 'I can't do that!' Was that what he expected his women-friends to do? To break dates for him? She resolved to ring up her friend Pamela first thing in the morning and make a date for the theatre in the evening.

The black eyes gleamed in the darkness. Was he put out? Or surprised that she hadn't caved in and promised to break her date? 'Tell you what,' he said slowly. 'I'll go sailing on Sunday instead of tomorrow. Come with me then, Tess.'

She drew in a quivering breath. Piers Branson, changing *his* arrangements? For a *woman*? Was that a first? Or—her eyes narrowed—was it simply that, when Piers Branson was in pursuit mode, he'd go to any lengths to catch the woman he was after?

But once caught—once he'd had his rakish way with her—how long would his interest in her last? For only as long as the chase lasted?

I'll give him a chase, Tess vowed. Piers Branson needs a woman who can give him a run for his money. Someone who'll be a real challenge to him. And I'm just the one who can do it! With what's at stake for me, I can remain objective...because I know I won't...can't—*mustn't*—get involved.

Oh, no? mocked a voice from deep down inside her. Remember that kiss?

She compressed her lips. Remembering it, she thought spiritedly, is precisely what will protect me. Forewarned is forearmed! There will be no more kisses!

But, having let him kiss her once, how could she refuse him the next time, without making him turn away from her in exasperation, getting bored with the chase? There would always be other women waiting in the wings for a man like Piers Branson. And he would be well aware of it!

'I've never actually sailed before,' she admitted after a moment, deliberately not jumping at his offer. But not turning it down either. 'You might find me a liability.'

'I'm sure, Tess, that you're a quick learner.' His teeth gleamed white in the night glow. 'I'll pick you up at eight-thirty Sunday morning. That too early for you?'

'I'll be ready. Eight-thirty on the dot.' Not eight minutes past, her eyes taunted him.

'On the dot. Yes, ma'am! Bring sunburn cream, a hat, and your swimming togs.'

She stood and watched him go, his tall, lithe frame swinging away with natural grace, his black dinner-jacket quickly merging into the darkness. Under the glow of the street-light outside, where he had left his car, he turned and waved to her, as if he knew she was still standing there watching him. Not that he could possibly see her—could he?—since she hadn't put the porch light on.

She felt a ripple of exhilaration, mingled with a faint trepidation. The kind of feeling she hadn't had since her first-ever date—or since last sitting for an important exam. She knew that, whatever lay ahead, it was now up to her.

Piers Branson was hooked. From now on, it was going to be a delicate juggling act. A real test of her ingenuity and cunning. Holding him at bay on the one hand...while still keeping his interest on the other.

She was almost looking forward to it.

She preferred not to think about, not even consider the possibility that she could be in any way hooked herself!

CHAPTER FIVE

'WON'T you be too hot in trousers?' Piers asked when he picked her up on Sunday— this time arriving on the dot, his black eyes flickering in sardonic acknowledgement when he found her ready and waiting.

'If it gets too hot later,' Tess said airily, knowing it was more than likely to, since there wasn't a cloud in the sky and the early morning sun was already warm, 'I can always change.' She indicated the bag on her shoulder, where she'd jammed in her hat, shorts, sunburn cream, and a swimsuit and towel. The truth was, the thought of Piers ogling her long legs all the way to the yacht club had been the deciding factor in what she was wearing now. Even though her own eyes were finding it hard not to ogle *his* legs, as they thrust in all their bronzed, well-muscled splendour from his white shorts, let alone his strong tanned arms with their brush of smooth dark hair, protruding from his navy polo shirt.

When they arrived at the marina, the place was already abuzz with activity. Tess surveyed the sea of masts and gleaming white hulls and wondered which boat belonged to Piers. The most spectacular one, no doubt!

'Well, this is it,' Piers said a few moments later, waving a hand.

Tess carefully hid her surprise. She had been expecting something huge and flashy, along the lines of Julius Branson's palatial state of the art motor-yacht. But Piers's yacht, while sleek and clean-lined, was relatively modest in size, not ostentatious in any way.

'Pretty, isn't she?' He made no attempt to conceal the pride in his voice, his eyes gliding over the yacht's smooth white lines with a warm, caressing tenderness that made her throat prickle with sudden heat. She wondered how it would feel to have his eyes run over her in the same way.

'She's easy to handle...which is what I like about her. I can sail her alone. And she's great to race. She responds just the way you hope she will...' There was a silky thread in his voice now, and a wicked glitter in the dark eyes as he caught her hand and helped her aboard.

Dear heaven! she thought with a flash of her eyes, their deep blue picking up the dazzle of the sun on the water. He's not just describing his boat . . . he's describing the kind of *woman* he likes! Easy to handle, eh? Responds just the way he hopes? Well, Piers Branson, she promised him under her breath, instantly rising to the challenge, you won't find this lady an easy ride, I can tell you!

'You race often?' she asked sweetly, rescuing her hand from his when he didn't seem anxious to let it go.

'Most weekends,' he said. 'Look, why don't you put your things down below, grab a hat, and then come up and adorn the bow while I take her out?'

Adorn the bow? Tess tossed her head, her tumble of curls glinting like red fire in the sun. 'Find some other adornment! You can show me the ropes—excuse the pun—and I'll lend you a hand.'

The black eyes danced, glinting into hers, whether in appreciation of her pun, or in amusement at the idea of her giving him a helping hand, she couldn't be sure.

'So you've never sailed before?' His tone was gently mocking.

'There's always a first time!' She waved an airy hand. 'I've had other things to keep me busy these past few years.'

'Andrew doesn't sail?'

She shot him a narrowed look. Was he being patronising? In his world, no doubt, everyone sailed from birth! And why did he have to persist in bringing up Andrew's name?

'Not everyone has the leisure or the means that you seem to have an endless supply of!' she heard herself snapping back, still feeling a bit raw over the way she'd dismissed Andrew so abruptly from her life. And at Piers too, for assuming that everyone spent their leisure hours out sailing their boats.

But the second the words were out she felt like biting her tongue. Fool, she berated herself, to risk alienating Piers at this delicate stage in their... friendship. But to apologise, or show any sign of mortification, would only weaken her in his eyes. He must have people forever kowtowing to him, and crawling up to him. And he probably despised them for it. No—no way would she grovel. She would make light of it. Make it into a joke!

She deliberately caught his eye and let him see the twinkling laughter in her own. If he has a sense of humour, she thought, he'll respond. If not, she might as well wave him goodbye right here and now!

She held her breath for a second—until she saw an answering light shimmering in the black depths, a smile tipping the corners of his mouth. Relieved—even faintly surprised to find that he shared a similar sense of humour—she smilingly turned her back on him, and headed for the cabin below.

When she emerged, she had her wayward curls confined under a practical peaked cap and her face and arms plastered with blockout. True to her word, she insisted on doing what she could to help, from hauling in lines to helping Piers hoist the sail. He might have been amused at her fumbling attempts to be of help, but he seemed to appreciate it, passing a wry remark about women normally preferring to sit and preen themselves on the bow, leaving him to do all the hard work.

Behind them the city gradually receded and, looking back, it was like looking at the buildings through a sheet of plate glass. Other boats skimmed by, some perilously close, and Piers needed to be constantly alert. Tess threw back her head and let the fresh breeze blow

into her face, enjoying the new sensation—
and enjoying the sight of Piers as well, tough
and capable at the helm, his dark hair tousled,
his strong profile outlined against the clear
blue sky, putting thoughts of pirates and buc-
caneers into her mind.

Around noon Piers dropped sail, and
moored at a small wharf below a rambling
multi-tiered harbourside house, with a tennis-
court and a swimming-pool cut into the rocky
slope below the house.

'My old family home,' he told her, an
eyebrow lifting as he glanced at her. 'My
parents still live here, when they're in Sydney.
I live in the upper flat of that double
apartment block next door, which we built on
part of our property. Phoebe lives in the lower
flat, and intends to stay on there with Tom,
after they get married.'

'What a spectacular position,' Tess murmured, glancing up at him. His eyes were still
on her, she noted nervously, the bright sunlight making him squint, veiling his expression. But even so...

She felt her hands growing clammy. Was he
thinking of inviting her into his private lair?
She flicked a glance across at his old family

home, assuming a polite interest. So...Julius Branson lived in that house. When he was in Sydney. She sucked in her breath, cursing the missed opportunity. If Julius hadn't gone off to his private island this weekend to re-cuperate, he might have been here in this very house today, and Piers might have taken her in to meet him. Damn, damn, damn, she thought—and immediately chided herself for being so selfish and unfeeling. The poor man was recovering from an operation, for heaven's sake! She ought to be thinking of him—he must still be feeling very sore and sorry.

'Penny for your thoughts, Tess.' Piers was still watching her—she could feel his eyes burning into her face. 'You're looking very pensive. Like to go ashore, would you, and take a look at my old home? The views, as you can imagine, are superb.'

'No!' she cried, and flushed guiltily, be-cause she knew she would have jumped at the offer had Julius been at home. 'I mean —— '

'I know what you mean, Tess. Relax. I didn't have any ulterior purpose in mind, I assure you. At least —— ' the black eyes glinted wickedly ' —— not without your consent! I just thought you might have liked to see the house...and the views. Honey's there—we wouldn't be alone.'

'*Honey*?' Tess echoed.

Piers's lip curved. 'Mrs Honey, to be precise. She looks after the place for Jules and Dee. And pops in next door to clean my place and Phoebe's once a week.'

'That must be quite an undertaking,' Tess murmured, her gaze moving from the sprawling family home to the narrow four-tiered apartment block next door. Both places had huge picture windows and broad balconies at each level, giving them sweeping views over the harbour.

'She has Joe to help her—*Mr* Honey. And a married daughter who comes in to help when needed. Joe takes care of the garden, and does any heavy work in the house. So...' Piers paused, looking down at her. 'Would you like to go in and take a look or not?'

She hesitated. If he meant to show her over the whole place, she just might happen to see some colour photographs of Julius, taken over the years. A glimpse of a likeness—a glimpse of red hair—that could be just what she needed to lift her spirits and spur her on.

But on the other hand...

'Maybe another time,' she said, making up her mind. The way Piers was looking at her... Yes, it would be far safer, at this point, staying out here on the harbour! Once he had her in that vast house, or if he managed to lure her under some pretext into his own apartment next door... No, she couldn't take the risk! If he tried anything... Not that it was the thought of fighting him off that was holding her back—it was that she might not want to. And that was something that mustn't happen. Getting emotionally involved with Piers Branson, while her relationship with Julius Branson remained unresolved, could lead to heaven knew what complications!

'OK...we'll have lunch on board,' Piers said cheerfully. He waved her towards the cabin. 'After you! We'll eat down below... out of the sun's heat.'

She felt sweat prickling her upper lip as she climbed down ahead of him, hoping she wasn't leaping from the frying-pan into the fire. The cabin down below was very small, very intimate...and very, very cosy!

Piers produced a bottle of wine from a tiny fridge, and a picnic lunch from the cool-box he'd brought on board with him.

'Honey's special ploughman's lunch,' he announced, revealing chunks of cheese and various cold meats, and crisp bread rolls.

'Great, I'm starving!' Tess confessed. 'It must be all this fresh air!' She slid in behind the tiny table, and after Piers had found plates and poured the wine he wriggled into the seat opposite. Over lunch she asked him about his life with the Bransons, and learned that before beginning his law degree at university, Julius had sent him up north to his cattle-station to work for a year as a jackaroo.

'Julius believes it toughens one up to work on the land,' he commented.

'And did it?' she asked. He did look tough, she realised. He might have led a pampered life, with every privilege imaginable, but it didn't appear to have softened him up—either his mind or his body. He exuded strength, a sharp intelligence, and—something that had been sadly lacking in Andrew—a healthy sense of humour.

He shrugged, a rueful smile tugging at his lips. 'Physically... and mentally. Everyone

should do it. It certainly broadens the education. Toughens mind, body and soul. I enjoyed my time up there...though I was
damned glad to get back.'

'Back to the city fleshpots?' she asked
teasingly.

He tilted his head at her. 'Is that what you'd
want to get back to, Tess?' he asked, in a bantering tone to match hers. 'The bright lights?
Life in the fast lane?'

She was about to deny it emphatically, but
caught the words back in time. 'I've never
really known a life like that,' she admitted,
carefully picking her words. 'Bright lights—
life in the fast lane—balmy tropical holidays...' Afraid that she might have gone too
far there, she reached for her wine-glass to
avoid that far too disconcerting gaze. 'I've
spent too much time with my head buried in
textbooks and doctors' rooms,' she added
with a careless jerk of her shoulder.

'You've never had a tropical holiday?' Piers
sounded surprised. Or aghast, more likely!

She toyed with her glass, aware that her
heart had picked up a beat. 'I had a holiday
on the Gold Coast once. Surfers' Paradise.
But——' she took a quick breath '—I'd prefer

to go somewhere less commercialised next time. Somewhere natural— unspoiled, peaceful. Maybe one of the islands— Hayman, Hamilton...' Her heart thumped in her chest. 'Except that a lot of those places are very commercial too these days. *And* expensive.'

Having sown her little seed, she wriggled out of her seat and gathered up the empty plates and glasses, carrying them over to the tiny sink. She gasped as she felt Piers's arms curl round her waist from behind.

Ducking sideways, she slipped from his grasp with a trill of laughter. 'I'm going to change,' she said, trying not to look at him. The sight of him, so raw and masculine, in this cosy, confined space, and the memory of his long legs brushing against hers from behind a moment ago, were unnerving her. 'I might take a quick dip while we're here. It's getting awfully hot!' She hadn't noticed it until now. But suddenly her whole body felt as if it had broken into a raging sweat.

'What, go swimming on top of all that wine?' Piers drawled.

'You shouldn't have drunk so much!' she scoffed. '*I'm* feeling fine!' She grabbed her bag and escaped into the pint-sized bathroom.

He was nowhere in sight when she came out, but when she climbed out on to the deck he was there waiting for her, wearing brief black bathing-trunks. Heat flared up her throat into her cheeks at the sight of him— reaching searing proportions as she felt his eyes on *her* as she peeled off the shirt she'd thrown casually over her black, high-legged swimsuit. She cooled off in the only way possible. She climbed the rail and dropped into the water.

Before she hit the surface, he was in the water too, diving in beside her, clean as a knife. They emerged together, laughing and blinking as water poured down their faces, his hands on her arms, his long muscular legs tangling with hers. She challenged him to a race, which was a foolish thing to do because she knew she'd have no hope of outdistancing him.

'If I catch you, I'm claiming a kiss!' he yelled after her.

He did catch her, of course, without any trouble at all, and claimed his kiss, the wildest, wettest, most erotic kiss she had ever experienced, broken only—mercifully, perhaps—when they both slid under the surface together, and came up gasping for air. After a laughing tussle, during which she managed to gather her lost wits, she broke away from him and struck back towards the boat in a flurry of white froth.

When she felt his hands on her shoulder she gave a shriek. 'I'm getting cramp!' she yelped, desperation in her eyes. 'Help me back on board!'

As she collapsed, panting, on to the deck, she moaned between gasps, 'I'm dead! You've killed me!'

'How's the cramp?' Piers asked, standing over her, water rolling down his tanned limbs, his mouth pursed in a mocking smile, his eyes openly sceptical.

Glancing up at him, she was unable to prevent the twinkling laughter that crept into her own eyes. 'Oh, it's fine...*now*,' she said, an impish grin curving her lips.

'You little devil, I don't believe you——'

'Toss me my towel, will you?' she begged, still lying flat on the deck, still gulping in deep draughts of air. 'I don't think I can move. I don't think I'll ever move again. I haven't used up so much energy for years!'

He scooped up her towel and dangled it from his fingers. 'What will you give me for it?' he teased, holding it just out of her reach. 'Another kiss?'

'You need to learn that everything you want, Piers Branson, doesn't get handed to you on a platter!' she choked back at him. 'Besides...you're spoilt enough already. It won't hurt you to go without something you want, for once.'

'Spoilt, am I?' Dropping to his knees beside her, he started dabbing at her shoulders and legs with her towel. There wasn't much room—his bare thigh was jammed up against her left leg. As she felt his hair-roughened skin touching hers, sending tingles of warmth through her, warning bells jangled. She sat up abruptly.

'I'll get burnt if I stay out here on deck!' She snatched the towel from him. Still breathless, she bundled it around herself and scrambled to her feet. 'I'm going to get dressed!'

While she was down below she heard the engine kick to life, and when she appeared on deck again Piers had pulled on his shorts and shirt and was unlooping the mooring rope, ready to move off. Once out in the harbour again, he hoisted the sail.

All in all, it was a fun day. She sensed that Piers was enjoying it as much as she was. Or was it the *chase* he was enjoying? she ruefully pondered.

On the drive back to her place later, Piers commented, almost in surprise, 'I haven't relaxed so much, laughed so much, *enjoyed* myself so much, for a long time.'

Aware of a flutter of pleasure, she said lightly, injecting a bantering note, 'I'm glad to see that you can enjoy a few simple, natural pleasures.'

He turned his head to smile at her—a slow, enigmatic smile. Of self-satisfaction? 'And it's good to see you enjoying a few things you've never experienced before, Tess—like going sailing... and enjoying gala performances at the opera... and—' he quirked an eyebrow '—dining in style.'

'Dining in style?' she echoed, not understanding. 'You're talking about our ploughman's lunch?'

He laughed. 'Not exactly...though I'm not knocking that. I'm talking about tomorrow night. I'd like to take you to Kables, Tess. Ever been there?'

Tomorrow night... She swallowed. He wasn't wasting any time! But then...wasn't this precisely what she'd been hoping for? To catch and hold his interest? It was only next weekend, less than a week away, that he would be flying up to see his father. If she wanted him to take her with him...

'No-o,' she admitted slowly. 'But...I thought you were in the middle of a big court case?'

'That's during the day—this is the evening. And the night is ours, Tess. Don't say no!'

She ought to say no. She ought to stop this here and now. Leading him on like this...simply to get a meeting with Julius Branson. It didn't matter that he might want only one thing of her, or that he would probably ditch her the moment she gave it to him. It didn't feel right. It *wasn't* right. Pretending that she was interested in him. Pretending that she enjoyed the pampered lifestyle that came so naturally to him.

Pretending that she wanted a tropical holiday. It was... It was underhand and despicable!

But how else would she ever get to meet the reclusive Julius Branson? How else would she ever find out the truth about her father? Piers Branson would survive—it might even do him good to find out that all women weren't after him. Or his millions.

'Well...maybe,' she said at length, knowing full well that she wasn't going to say no. And knowing, in her heart of hearts, that she didn't *want* to say no.

Satisfied, he murmured, 'How about we pick up some take-away on the way home...and eat it at your place? I won't stay long,' he promised, his eyes on the road ahead. 'I have some reading to do. Something I need to check up on before tomorrow.'

What did he mean by not long? She felt a flare of panic. Even five minutes, in her cosy little house, could be too long! She didn't trust him. Or herself, for that matter. The memory of those highly erotic, watery kisses this afternoon was still vivid in her mind! No... Somehow, between now and next weekend, she had to avoid private, secluded places when Piers was with her!

She sighed. 'Mind if I take a raincheck, Piers? I'm pooped. I'd like to take a long, soaking bath. And I must wash my hair. I'll just grab some salad from the fridge and then call it a day I think. I've got a bit of a headache,' she added for good measure. 'A touch of the sun, I guess.'

'No problem.' He seemed amused. Not a sign of sympathy! He didn't believe in her headache, obviously. And no wonder! She could *feel* the healthy glow in her face, could *feel* the lively sparkle in her eyes, could *feel* the smile of a day's pure enjoyment tugging at her lips. Stupid to lay it on so thick!

When he pulled up outside her unit she had already gathered up her things in readiness to leap out, just in case he changed his mind and insisted on seeing her to the door...and then, maybe, on coming in...just for a minute...or two...or three.

Turning to thank him, she saw his hand on the door and said quickly, 'No need to get out!' as she flung open her door and leapt out. 'Thanks for a great day. Bye!' she called over her shoulder as she made a dive for her gate.

Just as she reached it she saw someone else approaching in long strides along the footpath. And behind him, parked between two other cars, a familiar burgundy Volvo.

'Andrew!' she breathed, her mouth tightening. Her gaze leapt back to Piers's Jaguar, which hadn't yet had time to move away. In dismay, she saw him getting out. Oh, hell, she thought. Does he think I might need his protection?

'So...you did drop me for him!' Andrew accused, his eyes throwing daggers at both of them.

'Andrew, have you been spying on me?' she bit back at him. 'How long have you been here?'

His lip curled. 'Not all night and day, I assure you.' He laid stress on the word 'night'. 'I dropped in last night to see how you were, and found you weren't home. When I came back this morning, you still weren't home. You spent the night with him, didn't you?' he demanded savagely. 'And all day, by the look of you!'

'Oh, Andrew!' she snapped in exasperation. 'I've been out *sailing* all day. And last night I was out with Pamela. Go and ask her!

Not that I have to account for my movements to you. We parted ways, remember?'

'Oh, yes...you dropped me like a hot brick the second you saw a better prospect!' Andrew flicked a virulent look at Piers. 'Knowing damned well I can't offer you what a Branson can!'

Tess's cheeks flamed. Piers, she knew, could hear every word. By now he must think her a proper little gold-digger! 'It's a good thing we split up, Andrew,' she hissed back at him, deciding that attack was the best form of defence, 'because you obviously don't think much of me—let alone *know* me!'

Piers's smooth voice intervened. 'Nobody stole Tess away from you, Andrew. You didn't own her to begin with. Where's the wedding-ring? Where's the engagement-ring? You weren't even living together!'

Andrew glowered at him. 'You don't have to live with someone to be committed to them. We had an understanding!'

'We were just drifting along, you mean!' Tess corrected tartly.

'I asked you to *marry* me!'

'And I said no... because I didn't *want* to marry you. I wasn't sure of my feelings any more. I was so unsure, I wouldn't even move in with you—remember?'

'You soon made up your mind what you wanted,' Andrew grated, 'when dollar signs were dangled in front of your eyes!'

Tess drew in a sharp breath. How could she defend herself against that? It must look as if that was precisely what she *had* done! 'Andrew, go home,' she said wearily. 'It's pointless raking over dead coals.' She couldn't look at Piers. No doubt he'd be glad to see the last of her after this. 'I'm tired and headachey and I'm going in to take a bath!'

She swung away without a backward glance at either of them. Knowing, with a sinking heart, that it could well be the last time she ever saw or heard from Piers Branson again.

CHAPTER SIX

SHE wasn't sure what prompted her to do it, but the next day, after her morning clinic, Tess drove into the heart of the city and found a parking spot near the lawcourts. She wasn't sure if it was simple curiosity that made her want to watch Piers in action, or a tinge of desperation, born of the uncertainty she felt after last night! Piers had mentioned having dinner tonight, but that had been before Andrew had appeared. They'd parted without making any set plans, and after Andrew's spiteful barbs there might never be any set plans again—unless she took the initiative.

If Piers happened to catch sight of her in his courtroom, showing an interest in his case, it just might swing the pendulum her way. She tried not to think that it could just as easily work against her...convincing him that Andrew's comments about gold-diggers must have something in them after all, and that she was indeed chasing after him. For his money!

For that reason she dressed down, in a drab, shapeless top over a long skirt that wouldn't draw attention to herself, with a dark cap wedged down over her riot of bright Titian curls. And when she found the right courtroom, already packed with spectators, she slipped unobtrusively into the back row, where she sat waiting quietly for proceedings to start.

Piers's performance in court was an eye-opener. After what Andrew had said about him only marking time, only playing with the law, she had expected him to be appearing as a junior, assisting a more senior barrister, and she wouldn't have been surprised to see him lounging carelessly in a chair, twiddling with his pen, watching with a show of interest while trying to hide his boredom.

But Piers was the sole barrister defending the case. And he hadn't been exaggerating when he'd told her he had a major court case on. His client was a woman accused of murdering her husband after years of being beaten and abused by the man.

Tess barely recognised Piers at first, with his dark hair hidden under a solemn grey wig, and his athletic frame cloaked in layers of black. But, from the moment he opened his mouth, she was spellbound. His arguments were biting and to the point, his questioning of witnesses powerful, his interaction with the jury masterful. Glancing at the faces of the jury, she could feel their compassion for his client, could see it in their eyes, and in the way they hung on his every word. When she slipped out during a break in proceedings, to go back to her consulting-rooms, she had no doubt that he would win his case for the defence, if anyone could . . . and have his client acquitted.

Had he seen her? She couldn't be sure. He'd had his back to her when she left, and the rest of the time she'd been partially obscured by the people in front of her. All she could do now was to wait . . . and hope.

Each time the phone rang she jumped, expecting it to be him, even though she knew it couldn't be, because she knew he would still be in court.

By the time she headed home she was starving, having missed out on lunch to go to the courts. She pounced on her answering machine, holding her breath as she ran through the tape. When she heard his voice she nearly swooned with relief.

'Pick you up at seven-thirty. We're going to Kables, so wear something a bit more glamorous than that outfit you were wearing in court today.'

He'd seen her! She couldn't believe it. Was he going to berate her for slipping in so unobtrusively? Would he see it as spying on him? She groaned.

She made a special effort for that evening, taking extra care with her hair and make-up and choosing a dress she seldom wore because for one thing, it was in an eye-catching electric blue and, for another, it was very short and hugged her figure, and Andrew had complained, the only time she had worn it in his presence, that he hated it when she made an exhibition of herself.

'Everyone's staring. It's embarrassing. You're tall enough, without drawing *more* attention to your legs and your figure. Let alone your cleavage!'

Stung, having spent a small fortune on the dress, she had reminded him tartly, 'You told me to wear something bright and snappy because you wanted to show me off to your lawyer-friends. All *right*, I let my head go, for once. I won't inflict it on you again!' And she'd only worn it once since, to a wedding that Andrew had missed because he'd been away.

She stood uncertainly in front of her full-length mirror. Surely Piers Branson wouldn't feel uncomfortable with her in this dress? After all, it was a perfectly plain dress, really. It was just that it was very short, very bright, and the belt in the same fabric—which was plain too, neither shiny nor glittery—accentuated the narrowness of her waist, which in turn highlighted the curve of her hips. The dress was sleeveless, with narrow straps over the shoulders, and, though it did show some cleavage, the straight-across neckline was tasteful. Andrew had been exaggerating, as usual! She had decided to leave her throat bare of jewellery, so as not to draw attention to the hint of cleavage below. Though maybe, on reflection, a necklace might have drawn attention *away* from it...

No, she told herself in the next breath. Andrew's made you paranoid. There's no need to feel self-conscious. It's a perfect dress for a hot summer night, perfect for an up-market restaurant like Kables!

When the knock came on her door, she was waiting calmly.

'Wow!' Piers's black eyes gleamed, and she felt an instant qualm.

'Is it too bright?' she asked quickly. 'Too short?' Too sexy?

'Hell, no, it's a knockout. I reckon I've chosen the right place for you to show it off. Shall we go?'

Her smile wavered as she followed him out. For you to show it off... Was that what he thought she wanted to do? 'Actually, I seldom wear it,' she decided he should know. 'I hate drawing attention to myself.' It was Piers's eye alone she had wanted to catch. Not the eye of all and sundry!

He lifted an eyebrow. Underneath, the wicked black eyes gleamed. 'If I'd known that, I'd have taken you back to my place and called the caterers in. Because I assure you, Tess, you're going to be a magnet for all eyes where we're going.'

At the thought of an intimate evening at his place, she felt her pulses leap. The restaurant would be far safer, ogling eyes or not! With

Piers, on his own, there were far too many temptations. Not only for him...

'I'll try not to buckle under,' she assured him with a careless toss of her head.

'That I'd like to see,' he responded smoothly, a meaningful glint in his eye.

The other diners at Kables were far too polite to ogle, but there were plenty of surreptitious glances as they were led to their table. Champagne in an ice-bucket magically appeared.

'Just half a glass,' Tess insisted as Piers nodded to the waiter to do the honours. 'I seldom drink during the week, if I'm working next morning. And champagne goes straight to my head.'

'That's an intriguing prospect,' Piers remarked, the searing look he ran over her making her feel hot and tingly all over. 'How about I order some iced water as well?'

As they settled down to their meal she was grateful to him for not insisting on refilling her glass after she'd sipped it dry. Whenever Andrew had bought an expensive bottle of wine, he'd always ignored her protests and had kept topping up her glass until the bottle was finished.

'I hope you didn't mind me coming to watch you in court,' she said, watching Piers's face for his reaction. 'I didn't realise you'd seen me.'

'Oh, I don't miss much in my courtroom,' he said. His smile held a tinge of arrogance—which she guessed was what a good barrister needed. 'And no, why should I mind? I was flattered. Did the case interest you?'

'Very much. I felt so sorry for that poor woman—she was obviously driven to it, after being beaten and brutalised for all those years. She looked as if she was still in shock. I'm sure the jury are sympathetic too.'

'At the moment they're on her side. Let's just hope the prosecution doesn't pull any last-minute surprises before it winds up—hopefully within the next two or three days,' Piers said.

'You mean—like producing witnesses who'll try to blacken her name?'

'Anything's possible.' Piers held her eyes for a moment, looking at her with a new intentness. It was hard to tell if the look hid surprise, a tolerant amusement, or even a tinge, perhaps, of respect.

'Well, I wish you luck,' she said, taking a sip of cold water. Piers had ordered a Hunter Valley Chablis with their dinner and she'd already had half a glass of that, on top of the champagne. 'I hope she gets off.' Then she added, impulsively, 'You're handling it very sensitively. Your arguments...' She paused, about to say, took my breath away, but, not wanting to gush, she said instead, 'Were far more powerful than any the prosecution came up with.'

But it wasn't only his arguments that had impressed her. It was his voice, his mannerisms, the sheer force of his delivery. What a loss he was going to be to the legal profession when his father died, or retired, and he had to take full control of the Branson media empire.

'Won't you find it hard to give it up when the time comes?' she heard herself asking him. And drew in her breath when he shrugged, seeming loath to answer. 'I mean— when you take over your father's media business,' she pressed, her eyes wavering under his.

He was looking at her in a way she couldn't even begin to read. Was she showing too much interest in him? Piers Branson, she imagined, was a man who would prefer to do all the running with a woman, not be swept along, or manipulated, by *her*. If he thought a girl was getting too interested... or, heaven forbid, was chasing after him for the riches he could provide...

But sheer curiosity, the need to know how he felt about his future obligations, prompted her on. 'You are planning to give up the law, aren't you?' she asked slowly, hoping as she asked that he would say no, that what she'd heard wasn't true, that somehow he would find a way to keep his brilliant career as a barrister going. It would be such a waste if he didn't.

He was frowning down at his glass now, his fingers toying with the delicate crystal stem. 'Well... I can't do both,' he said with another brief jerk of his shoulder. Making it obvious he didn't think it was any of her damned business!

'No, of course not,' she agreed, and, burying her disappointment—was he going to toss it in, just like that?—she hastily switched to a more neutral topic. She didn't want to scare him off by appearing to criticise him or, worse, appearing too interested in him. He might think she was getting serious about him!

When he drove her home and pulled up at her gate, he asked if he could come in, causing her heart to flip in a double somersault. After a moment's hesitation, anxious to regain lost ground, she nodded.

'Just coffee,' she spelt out as she opened her front door and let him in.

He gave an ironic smile, his eyebrow lifting. 'This isn't a first date, Tess—or even a second. How long are you going to make me wait for a proper kiss?'

Her heart skipped a beat. Too late she wondered if she had been crazy to invite him in. She knew what he wanted, what a kiss would lead to. Piers Branson hadn't acquired a reputation as playboy of the western world because he liked drinking coffee! She eyed him sceptically, her soft lips curving. 'If I thought you'd be satisfied with a kiss...' At the thought of him kissing her—and what did he mean by a *proper* kiss?—her heart picked up its lost beat and began to thunder inside her.

Suddenly he whirled her round to face him, his hands hot on her bare shoulders. A sigh whispered from her lips. She didn't want to struggle, she realised, didn't want to break away. She even lifted her face to his. She could feel the tension in the air between them...could feel her scruples, her fine intentions, flying out of the window.

He took her face in his hands. His lips, achingly close to hers, were sensuous and inviting. 'Never fear, Tess—I *always* find your kisses satisfying,' he quipped, in a voice like softest silk.

Her lips parted. 'I meant——' But she got no further, his mouth stifling the words she had been about to utter.

For the next few seconds she was lost in a swirl of sensation, his kiss blotting out all reality, all common sense. It was only when she felt herself sinking into the realms of mindless euphoria, and realised with a shock that her body was straining against his, clamouring for more and more sensation, that she saw where she was heading and, with a gigantic struggle to regain her lost senses, she flattened her palms against his chest and pushed him away.

'There!' she gasped, her heartbeat thudding in her ears. 'You can't say that wasn't a proper kiss!' She looked up at him, with dazed eyes still blurred with desire. Her swollen lips were smarting from his kiss, her tongue still tingling with the taste, the sensual feel, of his.

'I was contemplating a kiss that would go on all night, Tess.' Piers's voice was low, as seductive as pure velvet, his black eyes wickedly persuasive, his meaning plain.

She shook her head, even though her eyes felt as if they were drowning in his, and saying something quite different.

'Why are you trying so hard to fight it, Tess?' He ran a feather-like finger down her smooth white cheek. 'I know it's what you want. You ache for it, as much as I do.'

Heat lashed through her at the headily enticing prospect. Stupidly, weakly, all she could do was shake her head again. Was she afraid that if she opened her mouth to say no, the word yes would come out?

'Is it Andrew?' He rapped the question at her.

Her tongue unlocked. 'No! Of course not!' She gulped, flushing at her vehemence. 'That's over,' she assured him in a calmer tone. She tilted her chin. 'And despite what Andrew said last night, you had nothing to do with it!'

Piers raised an eyebrow, his black eyes probing hers. Didn't he believe her? 'Then ... what's holding you back, Tess?'

Her eyelashes fluttered away. 'I ... It's too soon,' she said weakly.

'Tess ...' He reached for her again and she leapt back with a stifled gasp, out of his reach. With a grimace, he let his hands drop away. 'We both know it's what we want, Tess. Why go on fighting it? We're not young innocents. We both know what we're doing. I'll take precautions, don't worry. I *want* you, Tess.' The seductive note intensified. 'I've never wanted anyone as much.'

She turned her head sharply away at that. Did he use those same words to every woman he wanted in his bed? Or maybe only the ones who needed a bit of extra persuasion?

'And what Piers Branson wants, he must have?' she mocked, and heard in dismay the huskiness in her voice. To cover it, she taunted, 'I don't suppose you've been denied anything you've wanted in your entire life!'

She was playing for time, hoping that an exchange of strong words might cool his ardour. And her own. Without, she hoped, driving him away altogether!

'There hasn't been much in my life that I've wanted as much as I want you, Tess,' Piers said fiercely, his black eyes burning into her wary blue ones.

She gave a quick, nervous laugh, and threw back recklessly, 'And once I give in to you, once I'm out of your system, you'll want something else! Or some*one* else!'

His eyelids drooped slightly. That, she thought with satisfaction, has given him pause for thought. But her satisfaction was tinged with a faint regret. She drew in a quavery breath, hoping her reckless retort hadn't implied that she was getting serious about him. The last thing she wanted was to scare him off!

When he finally spoke, it was in a curiously flat voice. 'If it's a deep and meaningful relationship you want, Tess, with a gold ring on your finger —— '

'No!' She yelped. 'I mean ...' She flushed, dismayed that she'd given him the wrong impression. He'd run a mile if he thought she had long-term designs on him, and then how would she ever get to meet Julius Branson? 'Piers ...' She appealed to him with all the power of her vivid blue eyes. 'Can't we just...have a bit of fun and see what happens? And I don't mean *that* kind of fun! N-Not yet!' she gasped, as he took that as an invitation and took a step towards her. His black eyes, though, were narrowed, veiled, impossible to read.

But underneath the flickering eyelids he was relieved. She could sense it. A second ago he had been as tense as a coiled spring, and now he wasn't. He no more wanted to get seriously involved than she did!

'Piers...I'm going to say goodnight,' she said firmly, swinging away from him and making for the front door. 'You have your trial in the morning, and I have patients.' She pulled open the door. '*Please*,' she begged, when he made no move towards it.

'You'll say yes in the end, Tess,' he said, with a smile like a prowling tiger, sure of its prey. She forced a smile of her own, a gleam of resolve deepening the blue of her eyes.

'Give me a week, Piers,' she pleaded. 'A bit more time to get to know each other...' It was a gamble, laying down conditions to a man she'd a moment ago accused of being spoilt and always getting whatever he wanted. He was just as likely to laugh in her face and remind her that there were plenty of other fish in the sea—easier, more delectable fish, and all his for the taking!

And then—she hid a grimace—she'd have to find some other way to get to Julius Branson . . . though heaven knew how. At the same time she felt an odd sense of desolation that she knew had nothing to do with Julius Branson. Damn it, she *enjoyed* Piers Branson's company—sexual attraction aside. He was intelligent, exciting, stimulating to be with, never boring, the many facets to his character continually surprising her. So he might well be a fun-loving playboy with no intention of settling down in the foreseeable future, a wealthy high-flyer, who was far too sure of himself and his sexual powers—but he did take some things seriously. His work as a barrister, his clients, and even, she was sure, the family media business, since he already spent a good slice of his time working for his father. And at weekends he seemed to prefer sailing, racing his boat, to socialising with the élite set on board boats like his father's mega-yacht. As for that VIP gala night, he'd only attended it to impress her, not because he'd wanted to strut around and be seen there himself.

Piers took a step towards her, and she tensed. But this time he didn't attempt to take her in his arms. He merely reached out and touched a hand to her cheek. Which was enough to cause a sharp intake of her breath.

'OK, Tess—no more pressuring for a week.' He smiled, and again she was reminded of a tiger on the prowl. 'But you'll crack before then...I promise you.' And, with that, he swung round and disappeared into the night.

For the remainder of the week, a day didn't pass without her seeing or hearing from Piers. They swapped news on their day's doings and met when they could, either for dinner or for a few snatched moments when they were free during the day. Piers admitted that, in addition to the trial, which was drawing to a close and going well, he was keeping a close eye on his father's business while Julius was up north recuperating. Tess wondered how he managed to do all that he did, and still have time for her. She recalled what Andrew had said about Piers only playing with the law, only playing with the family business, simply liking to play, full stop. And had to wonder if there was something in that, after all—if he was just biding his time, dabbling with both careers, until the time came to take over his father's huge empire on a permanent, full-time basis. He certainly wouldn't be able to keep on with both, do full justice to two such demanding and totally different careers. It would be impossible. He'd admitted himself that he couldn't do both. When the time came, his promising legal career would have to end. It was a damned shame!

But that wasn't her concern. She had other things—more important to her—to worry about. As the weekend loomed nearer, and Piers's trial ended in a triumph for him, with the jury accepting his client's plea of self-defence and acquitting her, she became increasingly nervous and on edge. Would Piers fly off to the family island without her? Blowing her chance of a meeting with Julius?

She had to make sure he didn't! She had managed to get a week's grace from Piers—the idea being to keep him at arm's length until the weekend, hoping that by then she would be on his tropical island with him, and would know whether Julius Branson was her father or not. But what if she didn't meet Julius this weekend? Didn't get a chance to? She couldn't go on making use of Piers indefinitely—regardless of whether she gave in to him or not. It wasn't fair to him...even if he was only after her for one thing, and not the least bit likely to get emotionally involved.

She sighed, racked by qualms. Somehow things were threatening to get out of hand. She had never intended or expected to be so strongly attracted to Piers...or for him to be so seriously intent on pursuing *her*!

The sooner matters were brought to a head, the better. It certainly couldn't be soon enough for her!

Each time she had spoken to Piers during the week, or had met him for coffee or a meal, she had religiously enquired after his father—casually sprinkling the conversation with questions about the family island, and whether Piers's father was finding the tropical atmosphere therapeutic, and was he keeping in contact with his various companies, or was Piers taking control of everything while his father was convalescing?

To the last question Piers gave a soft chuckle. 'My father *always* has his finger on the pulse of everything that goes on. Even if he were lying on his death-bed, he would still have a phone clamped to his ear.'

Tess stifled a shudder at the thought of Julius Branson on his death-bed, and his secret, possibly, dying with him. 'You mean...he finds it hard to relax?' she asked, burning up with curiosity about him. She wanted to know everything!

'Oh, he takes holidays. He and my mother go away at least once a year—to Italy or Greece, or wherever their fancy takes them—and Tom and Phoebe and I keep things going in his absence. But if there are any major decisions to be made, Julius will be the one who makes them. Even if he's on the Italian Riviera at the time. He's always in contact by phone.'

'Don't you ever get frustrated, not being able to make any major decisions yourself, not being in full control?' she asked curiously. Was that why he spent so much time on his work as a barrister? To give him a feeling of being in control, at least in one area of his life?

Piers shrugged. 'I might not have a hands-on managerial position, but I have a number of directorships in the family companies—as all the family have—so we all get a say in decision-making. Why the concern, Tess? You'd like to see me taking full control, would you?' he asked with a lopsided smile. But there was a glint of something in his eyes that she couldn't read.

'Good heavens, no!' she cried. 'That would mean your father would be—that he —— ' she bit her lip as she realised she could possibly be talking about the death of her own father! 'Piers, I—I didn't mean that I wanted... That your father —— ' She broke off, exasperated with herself for the way she was floundering. She tried to laugh it off. 'He's recuperating from a gall-bladder operation, not suffering a life-threatening disease! I'm sure he's going to live for a long time yet. I hope!' she added fervently.

Too fervently, she realised with a faint qualm. Piers was looking at her very oddly.

'Would you like to meet him, Tess?'

She gaped at him. 'Wh-what do you mean?' she heard herself stammering. 'He—he's up north.'

She expected him to say that he'd meant when his father was recovered and back in

Sydney. She could hardly believe it when he said instead, 'That's right. Where I happen to be going at the weekend. You could come with me, Tess.'

She caught her breath. It was an effort to hide her elation. 'I—I...' She didn't want to appear too eager.

'I'm flying up to Rockhampton on Friday—tomorrow mid-morning, that is. Julius is sending the helicopter to pick me up from there. We can come back late Sunday, or even Monday.' His eyebrow shot up. 'Any hope of taking next Monday off, Tess? It would give us an extra day up there.'

She thought quickly. 'I only have surgery in the afternoon. I could try to rearrange my appointments.' She was astonished at herself. Putting off patients! That was something she had never even considered doing before. Would Piers wonder why she had jumped so readily at his invitation? She hid a sigh. He'll think I'm doing it for him—what else can he think?

'Well, if you can't,' Piers said easily, though he was still watching her with a disconcertingly hooded look, 'we could fly back Monday morning.'

'I'll let you know in the morning,' she promised. 'Um—have you told your father you might be bringing me with you?' If Julius Branson was her father, it would only be fair to prepare him. He must be familiar with her name, having sent money to her all these years. He might not *want* her to come.

'I told my mother. Told her I was hoping to bring an intelligent, attractive, charming lady rheumatologist with me. I also mentioned that you were a stunning redhead with a great sense of humour. My mother commented that it would be a nice change for me to bring home a girl with a bit of intelligence and humour, for once. My mother's very down-to-earth,' he added with a rueful smile, 'with a good sense of humour herself. Nothing fazes her.'

Tess sucked in a quivering breath. If nothing fazed Piers's mother, why had Julius Branson been so paranoid all these years about keeping his daughter a secret? Because she wasn't his daughter? Could Michael Lawrence possibly have been wrong?

But...how could he be wrong? Who else could it be? It had to be someone close enough to her mother to have cared about her future welfare—someone married and wealthy enough to put Tess through private schools and university, and to provide for her mother so that she didn't have to go back to work after Tess was born—which had been a real boon to her mother, with her crippling arthritis. And who else but Julius Branson, the boss who had taken her away travelling with him, had been so close to her, other than her husband? So maybe it *had* been more hush-money than caring or generosity, but it had been very generous hush-money. And for the lawyers to keep it a secret all these years... Surely few men other than Julius Branson would have the power, or the means...

'Why all the sighs?' Piers's amused voice broke into her thoughts. 'You're not nervous, Tess, surely?'

She laughed, flushing. She hadn't realised that Piers had been watching her so closely. 'Well, maybe—a bit,' she admitted. Why deny it? Most people outside Julius Branson's tight circle of family and friends would be nervous in the powerful magnate's presence. He had a reputation for being overpowering, intimidating, a formidable figure.

If Piers only knew just how nervous she was!

CHAPTER SEVEN

'WHAT'S the matter, Tess?' Piers shouted over the whirr of the engine. 'Never been in a helicopter before? You're tight as a spring.'

Tess gave a start as his hand covered hers, his touch making her aware of the way she was clutching the edge of her seat.

'No...never,' she told him, but it wasn't the flight that was making her tense, it was the thought of coming face to face at last with Julius Branson.

'What do you think of the view?' Piers asked, in an obvious attempt to take her mind off her edginess.

'Oh—fantastic!' she enthused, realising with a flush that, even though she had been watching the scene below with her eyes, she hadn't been consciously taking in the beauty of the vanishing Queensland coastline and the breathtaking expanse of sparkling water below. The different colorations in the water were amazing—iridescent opal-green merging into dazzling turquoise, deep cobalt shading to the palest aquamarine. She caught glimpses of reef-fringed islets and coral cays, dark splashes on the vivid water.

'Not far now,' Piers consoled her. 'See that dark shape ahead? Over there,' he said, pointing. 'That's Akama—our island.'

Tess felt her muscles tensing again, her eyes fixed on the dark shape that was growing larger and greener by the second. She could already pick out palm-trees on the sandy white shore.

'You did tell your parents about me?' she asked anxiously. 'They know my name and everything?'

She felt Piers's bemused gaze on her. 'Your name? Why? Should it mean something?'

'I...' Tess gulped. 'It's just that I—I wouldn't want to arrive unannounced—like an anonymous hanger-on!'

'Ah.' His lips spread in a grin. 'Rest assured, Tess, I told Dee all about you. She was more concerned about what *your* reaction might be...coming into a convalescent home, as she called it. What with my father, and my aunt...'

'Oh, yes.' Tess had forgotten all about his terminally ill aunt and felt a twinge of guilt for not enquiring earlier. 'How is your aunt?'

'Poor thing's getting weaker, but she's not one to whine or complain. She's the sweetest, bravest lady. She has a nurse, but my mother's doing her best to make her last days—or weeks, or whatever—as happy and comfortable as she can.'

'Your mother sounds a wonderful woman herself,' Tess said, swallowing a lump in her throat. A heaviness clamped over her heart at the thought of what she might be doing to this fine woman, should the truth of her birth inadvertently come out. What right had she to enter these people's lives, and risk disrupting their peace and their happiness?

But I don't want to do that—I won't do it! she vowed in silent protest. She simply wanted to *know*. To know who her father was. And should Julius Branson do the unthinkable and acknowledge her as his daughter—even if only between the two of them—that would be enough. It would give her a chance to thank him for what he had done for her and her mother, and to reassure him that she would go on guarding his secret, if that was the way he wanted it to remain, and bow out of his life...even though she knew that would mean bowing out of Piers's life too—a thought that caused her far more pain than she would have expected. But that was inevitable anyway— knowing Piers's fast-and-loose reputation with women.

Everything hinged, of course, on whether she had a chance to speak to Julius Branson in private. If not, at least she would be able to meet him at last. She would hear his voice, see his face, be able to note his mannerisms— and, above all, be able to look for signs of a likeness, or for some spark of recognition, or familiarity. And then at least she would *know*.

The helicopter landed on a heli-pad at the edge of the tropical forest, within a short walk of the family bungalow. Typical of houses in the tropical north, the Bransons' island home was set high off the ground, with timber-latticed verandas all around and shuttered French doors. It looked out over lush green lawns, shaded by tall palm-trees and mela-leucas, to sweeping views over the Whitsundays. Piers told her there were also a couple of secluded cabins near the house, built for the use of guests not staying with the family, or for anyone else they wished to accommodate.

'We'll be staying with your family, won't we?' she asked, flicking him an anxious glance. The moisture-laden air, filled with the trills and chirps and squawks of birds, was like a steam-bath, the air saturated with the burnt-treacle scent of the melaleulcas.

Piers quirked an eyebrow. 'Never fear, my dear Tess, you'll be amply chaperoned—we'll be staying at the house with Dee and Julius. The pilot tells me he's staying overnight in one of the cabins, and the crew of *Mistique*, which came up during the week, have the choice of using the other one or staying on the boat.'

No one came out to greet them, which Tess, in her edgy state, thought an ominous sign. Had Julius Branson, hearing that she was coming—if he was her father, he would have recognised her name—arranged for his family, under some pretext, to stay out of her sight? She gave herself an impatient shake. Now she was being ridiculous! How could he do that if she and Piers were staying in their home for the weekend?

When Piers reached for her bag, her uncertainty made her almost snap at him, 'I can carry it!' causing his eyebrow to rise a fraction higher.

'My family are not ogres, Tess.' He gave her a rallying smile, but there was a faintly bemused look in his eyes, as if it puzzled him, or surprised him, that she should be so up-tight about meeting his family.

When she saw a flat, harder light glint in the black depths, her heart sank. I suppose he thinks I'm so anxious to get my clutches into him that I'm afraid that if his family don't like me, don't approve of me, they won't give me their blessing!

But she could hardly tell him the real reason for her butterflies.

'Well...' She drew in a ragged breath, feeling she had to say something. 'Some people don't like outsiders coming into their home, especially when they're recovering from an illness, as your father is...or when there's a dying patient in the house.'

The black eyes appeared to soften. 'They know you're a doctor, Tess. They know you're not likely to do anything to upset anyone.'

'Yes...I suppose I'm being silly.'

She trailed after him up the timber staircase, across the deeply shaded veranda to the fanlit front door, which opened miraculously as they reached it, as if eyes had been watching their approach. A petite Filipino woman appeared, her delicate face breaking into smiles at the sight of Piers.

'Ah, Evelyn! How are you?' Piers greeted her. He stood aside to let Tess in ahead of him. 'Evelyn...this is my guest, Dr Keneally,' he said as they stepped inside, where they were immediately enveloped in a delicious coolness. 'Guest-room ready?'

Evelyn gave an indignant sniff. 'Of course. Isn't it always?'

Tess caught Piers's eye, and this time it was her eyebrow that rose. Not that she was surprised to learn that she wasn't the first guest Piers had brought to the Branson family's island hideaway! She let her gaze roam round the spacious entrance hall, taking in the polished parquetry floor, the brass pots overflowing with leafy plants, the yellow hyacinths thrusting from a decorative vase on a marble-topped console table. She glimpsed a tastefully furnished sitting-room off the hall, with patterned floor-rugs in various shades of blue. Cool, simple elegance. Not a sign of the opulence she had expected. No doubt the

Bransons reserved that for their grand Sydney mansion.

Evelyn plucked Tess's bag from her fingers, turning to Piers as she headed for a long passage off the hall. 'Mr Branson says that after you've freshened up you're to join him for drinks in the sitting-room.'

As Tess's heart gave a nervous flutter, Piers drawled, 'Oh, he's up and about then, is he?'

Evelyn gave a snort. 'You don't think you can keep Mr Branson in a sick-bed, do you?'

Piers grinned and, in spite of the tension gripping her, Tess found that she was smiling too. It was plain that Evelyn was not at all in awe of her high-powered employer. Perhaps he wasn't as formidable as the media liked to make out.

How would *she* react to him? Tess wondered, running a nervous tongue over her lips. Or, more to the point, how would he react to her?

Although she had been waiting for Piers's knock for the past five minutes, Tess jumped when it came.

'Tess, are you ready?'

She took a last fretful glance at her reflection in the long cheval mirror, belatedly wondering if she should have confined her riot of curls in some way, or worn something with a bit more colour, or something softer and more feminine, before she swung away with a sigh and reached for the door.

'You've changed.' Piers's dark gaze ran over her sleeveless black top with its deeply scooped neckline, and on down the full length of her blue denim skirt, which reached almost to her ankles. 'You didn't have to, you know. We're very casual here. Those trousers you had on before would've been fine.'

Tess's eyes leapt to his. 'You don't like what I have on?' As the question leapt out, she realised it was the first time in her life that she had asked for a man's opinion on the way she was dressed. Andrew had made a point of giving his opinion a few times, free of charge, but she'd never actively sought it.

'My dear Tess, you'd look stunning in a sack,' Piers said, which ought to have boosted her confidence, but didn't. He still hadn't commented on her skirt and top. And there was an almost guarded look in his eye that added to her disquiet.

As he ushered her through the house he made no attempt to tuck her arm through his, or to put a comforting hand on her elbow, barely even brushing against her. She wondered if maybe he didn't want Julius seeing them on any kind of intimate terms, and jumping to the erroneous idea that his playboy heir was seriously interested in his latest house-guest.

But that was the least of her worries right now!

Piers paused, standing aside to wave her into the sitting-room. Her legs felt stiff as she forced them to carry her in, her sandals making no sound on the richly patterned floor-rug. She could feel Piers right behind her, still not touching her.

She noticed nothing in the room, her gaze focusing on the man sitting in a deep armchair in front of the long French windows, the bright light behind him casting his face into shadow and making a silver halo of his hair.

She barely breathed as the man rose from his chair.

'Jules, no need to get up!' But Piers's protest came too late. Julius Branson was already on his feet, though his massive frame was slightly bowed, as if he was unable yet to straighten properly after his operation.

'I'm not an invalid!' he snapped. He didn't approach them. He waited for them to come to him. 'You've brought someone with you,' he growled. Tess felt her insides quaking. He wasn't smiling.

'Yes, Jules...' Piers stood back. 'I'd like you to meet Tess Keneally. She's a —— '

'A doctor. I know—Dee told me what she is!' Showing no reaction to her name, Julius held out his hand, forcing Tess to take a step closer to accept it. The handshake was firm but brief. Obviously he had no great wish to let it linger, let alone give it a meaningful squeeze. No wish to touch her.

'I hope you enjoy your visit,' he said, using polite but meaningless words, his tone abrupt, almost abrasive.

Shaken, she peered into his face, managing to dredge up the words, 'Thank you,' from the depths of her throat. Her voice sounded brittle, unlike her own. This isn't my father, she thought. It can't be. Not this cold, remote stranger.

Nothing about him sparked any sense of recognition or feeling of empathy. She had always imagined, since her mother had been fair-haired, that she must have inherited her red hair from her father. But this man's hair was completely white, his eyebrows the same, and though pale-faced—which was only to be expected after his recent surgery and confinement—he didn't appear to have the complexion of a redhead. His eyes, granted, were blue, but the palest blue, nothing like the vivid blue of her own.

'Tess has been anxious to meet you, Jules,' Piers said from behind her, and she could have turned round and kicked him, two bright spots of colour leaping to her cheeks.

'Oh?' Julius Branson eyed her coldly. No father, Tess thought miserably, could look at his daughter for the first time with such cold, unfriendly eyes. Certainly not a father who had cared about his daughter enough to pay for her education and upkeep for all these years, and was still sending her money twice a year.

Michael Lawrence had been mistaken. He'd assumed wrongly. It was obvious. She had made a terrible blunder dragging Piers into this...using him the way she had...

She drew in a deep breath. She would put him to one last test. Bring out her trump card.

'Well, yes,' she admitted, in a voice that was far calmer than she felt. 'I...believe you knew my mother, Mr Branson?'

'Your mother?' Not a flicker of reaction. Nothing but a polite, perhaps even slightly bored, enquiry.

Beside her she felt Piers stiffen, and her flush deepened. He must be wondering why she hadn't told him. She hadn't dared! If he had thought that she'd only sought his friendship so that she could meet Julius Branson, she was sure she wouldn't be here now. He would have ditched her on the spot.

'Rosalind Keneally,' she said succinctly, her eyes fixed to his face.

Julius frowned, as if casting back in his memory. The pale blue eyes didn't even waver!

'She used to work for you...as your private secretary,' Tess assisted. 'I know it's a long time ago. Before I was born. She worked for you for a number of years. She always told me you were a wonderful boss.' It was true.

Her mother had always spoken highly of him, without once intimating that there had been any kind of intimate relationship between them. Because one had never existed? She wondered with a plummeting heart.

'Before you were born...' Julius repeated slowly. 'We're going back, aren't we? Mmm... Oh, yes, now I remember,' he conceded, looking only marginally interested. 'I did have a secretary many years ago whose name was—that's right, Rosalind. Ros Keneally. She invited me to her wedding. Can't remember the guy's name... Malcolm? Michael? How *is* your father?' he asked with a tepid show of interest.

Tess felt a light-headedness sweeping over her. Julius Branson believed Michael Lawrence was her father! If Julius had fathered her, he would know that wasn't possible. Because whoever *had* fathered her would know that he had a daughter. Hadn't he been supporting her generously all these years since?

Her search, she realised bleakly, had come to a crashing, grinding halt.

She gave a start as she felt Piers's hand slide round her waist, giving her a comforting squeeze. 'Tess's mother divorced her husband, Jules, after he walked out on her around the time Tess was born. He wasn't Tess's father. He'd always refused point-blank to have children. That's why he left.'

Tess was grateful for Piers's supporting arm. If he hadn't been holding on to her, she doubted her legs would have kept her standing. But, even in her weakened state, her eyes never left Julius Branson's face, searching, in her misery, for a last glimmer of hope. No father, surely, could be so insensitive—so cruel—that he could hide it from her after this?

Her heart plunged like stone when she saw no change in his expression, just a grim, closed face, and a cold, icy withdrawal. His lip even held the hint of a sneer. As if he found it distasteful that his son and heir had brought home a girl with such a background. No known father. A divorced mother. In his eyes, no doubt, a deprived, sordid background.

And then Julius turned his back on her, lumbering over to a cabinet against the wall to top up his glass of whisky. 'What will you two have to drink?' he asked, without even glancing round.

Tess didn't really care. She knew she wouldn't taste it, whatever it was. But maybe she needed a slug of alcohol to dull the heavy ache of disappointment inside her.

'Scotch on the rocks for me, thanks,' Piers said. 'Tess? Whisky? Gin and tonic?'

'I'll have whisky too, thanks.'

Nothing more was said about her mother. Julius asked her no questions at all, in fact virtually ignored her. Tess wondered if he treated all Piers's female house-guests this way... or only certain ones. Women who didn't fit his idea of a suitable companion for his son and heir.

Lowering himself gingerly into his armchair, Julius answered Piers's questions about his health, asked a couple himself about the business, and then said, still looking at Piers, not at Tess, 'You'll be having lunch aboard *Mistique*. The crew plan to take you out to the outer reef. They're waiting for you now.'

Piers looked as if he was about to argue about that, but apparently decided against it. 'Are you and Dee coming with us?'

Julius gave a snort. 'Hardly. I've no wish to be buffeted about on a boat all afternoon. And Dee said she would see you at dinner.'

'I haven't even said hello to her yet.' Piers glanced round. 'Where is she?'

'She's giving your aunt her lunch. Poor Camille's having a bad day, and Dee's going to stay with her.'

'Can't the nurse look after her?' Piers asked, frowning. 'Dee will be running herself ragged, with two invalids to look after.'

'I'm not an invalid!' Julius snapped, and Piers winked at Tess, as if he'd known that was coming. 'I'm perfectly capable of looking after myself,' he grumbled. 'As for Camille's nurse, we had to fly her home for the weekend—she had a family wedding to go to. Your mother's perfectly happy. She was a nurse once herself, remember. She *likes* taking care of my sister-in-law.'

'Dee likes taking care of anybody who needs a bit of tender loving care,' Piers was swift to amend, his affection for Delia Branson plain to see. 'She's been caring for people for as long as I've known her—from the day Phoebe and I came into your lives.'

'Dee was already a second mother to you,' Julius reminded him gruffly, 'even before you came to live with us. Your parents often left you with us when they had business overseas.

And thank God they did that last time, or you might have been on that Mexican bus with them.' For the first time, Tess caught a glimmer of emotion in the pale blue eyes.

Piers, conscious that Julius was not including Tess in the conversation, explained for her benefit. 'My parents had gone to Mexico for a conference. On their weekend off they took a bus trip into the mountains. The bus,' he added, in a flat, controlled voice, 'plunged over a ravine, killing everyone on board.'

'Oh, Piers, how terrible!' Tess cried involuntarily, the blue of her eyes deepening in sympathy for him. But even as she felt for him, and for his sister Phoebe too, her mind couldn't shake off the haunting image of Delia Branson. She sounded an angel. A deeply caring, giving, loving woman, who could have been deeply hurt had Tess's suspicion about Julius Branson being her father proved true. No matter how carefully they'd tried to keep it from her, Dee was bound to have found out. The two were obviously very close.

Suddenly, despite the deep blow she'd suffered, and the black hole it had left in her heart, Tess was glad, even in an odd way relieved, that Julius Branson was not her father. Not for the world would she have wanted to risk hurting a woman as loved and loving as Delia Branson appeared to be.

And though she would never have admitted it—she hardly dared even think about it— she knew that deep down inside her there was another, more personal reason for that twinge of relief.

Tess leaned over the rail of *Mistique* with her face turned into the warm, seductive breeze, her eyes drinking in the crystal clarity of the rich turquoise water, her senses seduced by the sight of tropical islets and submerged reefs and the misty purple humps of other islands in the hazy distance. She lifted a hand to wave to another boat, and the two young couples on board, out enjoying the entrancement of the Whitsundays, waved back.

'I've never been anywhere so beautiful,' she breathed, leaning back, still holding on to the rail. 'This sure beats holidays at Manly Beach.'

'Is that where you normally spend your holidays?' Piers asked from beside her. 'At Manly?'

She turned to see if he was mocking her. Laughing at her. The wicked eyes were certainly dancing...but then, they usually were. She tilted her chin. 'No, not always. I've been to the Gold Coast as well, if you recall me telling you. And to Singapore, once. Not that there's anything wrong with Manly.' She'd had some great holidays there.

'I agree.' Now he wasn't even trying to hide his amusement. Having sensed her defensiveness, no doubt. 'I've sailed there many a time.'

She pursed her lips, her eyes narrowing as she peered into his deeply bronzed face. 'That's what you'd prefer to be doing right now...isn't it?' she asked shrewdly. 'Sailing. Zipping across the Whitsundays in your snazzy little yacht. This——' She waved a hand '—lounging idly around on a giant cruising-yacht isn't your idea of fun, is it? No challenge in it.'

He raised an eyebrow, and chuckled softly. 'Wrong!' His black eyes, glittering like polished ebony in the sharp sunlight, caught hers...and held them. 'I'm just where I want to be. With you. And you give me all the challenge I need.'

She raised an eyebrow of her own, trying not to think about the pleasurable flutter she felt inside. 'Do I, now?' Was that all she was to him? A challenge?

Suddenly, now that the spectre of Julius Branson was no longer between them, since he was obviously not her father, and now that there was no need any longer to keep Piers at arm's length, she dared to wonder what it would be like...

One of the uniformed crew, a tanned-face young man called John, had spread out an enticing lunch of fresh seafood and salad on a table on the rear deck. As they were eating, Tess realised that Piers was eyeing her oddly.

'Do I have lettuce between my teeth?' she asked, confused by the enigmatic look in his eye.

'No...you don't.' His lips tilted. 'Can't I just look at you? I *like* looking at you.'

'It wasn't that kind of a look,' she said with a wry smile. 'You looked as if you were... I don't know. Puzzled about something. Or curious. So...' She swallowed. 'Be my guest. Fire away.'

He gave a brief jerk of his shoulder. 'It was the way *you* were looking, Tess. You seemed a bit pensive, that was all. Some-thing...bothering you?'

She bit her lip. Piers saw more than she'd thought! His years as a barrister must have given him an insight into people's minds. 'I was just thinking...' She paused, sighing. 'Piers...I should never have come,' she said in a rush. Avoiding his eye, she half turned in her deck-chair and gazed out over the bril-liant water to a distant coral reef. 'I'm in-truding. Your father's not well. Your aunt's at death's door. Your mother has her hands full.' Abruptly, she swung back to face him. 'Why did you bring me?' The question burst out.

His eyes flickered under her heated gaze. 'I thought you *wanted* to come?'

She flushed. Had she made it that obvious? 'I—I did. Who wouldn't want to spend a weekend on a tropical island?' she said airily, mentally kicking herself for asking such a loaded question. She knew full well why Piers had brought her here. For his own rakish pleasure! And her readiness to come with him, whatever her true reason, had unwittingly given Piers the green light.

'Was that all it was, Tess?' The black eyes held hers, demanding an answer. 'Just the prospect of a relaxing tropical holiday weekend?'

A quiver rippled through her. 'I...' She wrenched her eyes away from the magnetic spell of his. 'Piers, I—I don't think your father wants me here,' she dragged out. It was better than dragging out an admission of another sort. 'He obviously doesn't like me. Doesn't approve of me.'

Piers gave a dismissive snort. 'That's just Jules. My father thinks all the women I bring home are after the Branson fortune, not me.'

All the women? So she was just the latest in a long line—Piers Branson's latest plaything. But she'd known that from the beginning. No need to feel so... So what? Down-hearted? *Jealous*? Was this pained feeling what being jealous felt like?

She forced a teasing smile to her lips. 'And you think I'm different, do you?' she challenged, a bravely taunting light in her eye.

Did she only imagine the fleeting pause before he answered? 'Tess, you're nothing like the others. You're...' He paused for a heart-stopping second. The black eyes, burning with an intensity she hadn't seen before, seemed to swallow her own. 'Damn it, Tess, do you think I'd care even if you were after the last cent I possess? I *want* you, Tess. I'm crazy about you!'

She felt something swoop inside her, arrowing right down to the pit of her stomach. Startled by it, and shaken equally as much by the intensity in his voice, his eyes, she snapped her gaze away from his.

When she felt his hand on her knee, she jumped as if he'd struck her.

'You don't exactly find me repulsive either . . . do you, Tess?'

Her eyes flew to his. Somehow, despite the chaos churning inside her, she forced a playful smile to her lips. 'Not exactly . . . repulsive, no,' she murmured, finding it an effort to keep her tone light.

She didn't know if she was relieved or dismayed when John reappeared at that moment with a platter of fresh tropical fruit. Piers drew back his hand.

'Tess . . .' He waited until John had moved away again, out of earshot. 'I'm still curious . . .'

'About what?' she asked huskily. There was an odd undercurrent in his voice now that made her vaguely uneasy. Without looking at him, she reached for a slice of mango and popped it into her mouth.

'Why didn't you tell me your mother used to work for Julius?' he asked quietly.

Her heart stopped. 'I...' She hesitated, gulping, her mind working overtime. Inspiration struck. 'I—I didn't want you to think I was using my mother's name to—to ingratiate myself into your family!'

'Oh, Tess.' He caught her hand and laced his fingers through hers. 'I might have known...' His mouth took on a rueful twist. 'I guess I've been around too many scheming females. Hypocrites, a lot of them. You're nothing like them, Tess.' He grinned suddenly. 'You're not the type to use people— let alone lick anyone's boots.'

Heat flamed across her cheeks. If he only knew! Bitterly ashamed of the way she had deceived him—*used* him—she glanced down at the fingers entwined in hers. 'Now you'll have sticky fingers,' she mumbled, summoning a smile. 'That was a disgustingly juicy mango.'

'Well...since I'm already sticky, why don't I offer you a piece of pineapple as well?' He reached out to pluck a slice of ripe golden pineapple from the table. 'Here—open your mouth.'

She obediently parted her lips, involuntarily leaning towards him. 'Mmm,' she murmured, as the pineapple's sweetness filled her mouth. But it was the sensuousness of Piers's fingers sliding between her lips that she found even more tantalising.

And why shouldn't I enjoy the sensation...and whatever other sensations he offers? she thought, rallying. She was free now...gloriously free of the restraints—personal, ethical, legal, whatever—that had previously held her back. Julius Branson was no longer between them!

It was a heady, liberating feeling, the realisation that she no longer had to hold back her feelings for him.

Only...was it *wise* to have feelings for Piers Branson? It was unlikely he had any intention of getting seriously involved himself. Certainly not on a long-term, let alone permanent, basis. Could she accept that? Live with it? She had never been one to play around, to go into a relationship without deep feelings on both sides, and at least some sense of commitment. Piers Branson wasn't into commitment. He'd told her so. 'If it's a deep and meaningful relationship you want, Tess, with a gold ring on your finger...' And he'd looked *anxious*, until she'd reassured him.

Besides which, he wasn't even her type. She despised rich, pampered playboys. And Piers Branson, mega-millionaire, mega-playboy, was the high-flying prince of them all, a man used to having whatever he wanted, whenever he wanted it, the world his oyster. But it wasn't her world. They came from totally different worlds, from totally different backgrounds. They had different friends, different values, different ideals. She was an ordinary hard-working doctor, with simple tastes, modest needs, and a serious outlook on life and commitment. Hardly *his* type.

Sure, he was attracted to her—physically. He'd made that abundantly plain. But was that what she wanted? To be his latest bedmate, his latest good-time girl, for however long his interest lasted? It might be enough for him, but she simply wasn't built that way. There had to be more.

And yet...

'Um...' Stepping out on deck to clear the table, John seemed reluctant to disturb them. 'You can see the outer reef now, Mr Branson. We'll be there shortly.'

Tess jumped up at once from her comfortable deck-chair. 'I'd better go down and wash off this stickiness,' she said, and quickly made her escape.

'We'll go snorkelling on the reef,' Piers called after her. 'You'd better change while you're down there.'

The afternoon was pure magic. It wasn't only the glories of the Great Barrier Reef—the fantastic shapes and colours of the coral, waving and twisting with the tide; the myriad tiny fish, glowing like jewels, flashing and darting in water as transparent as rock crystal—though all those things certainly enhanced the magic. It was being with Piers— snorkelling together hand in hand below the glassy surface, sharing the sights and sensations with him, feeling the warm water flowing over her body, then feeling his hands caressing her body in an even more sensuous way. And afterwards, exploring the reef together on foot, wearing sneakers to protect their feet from the stone-fish and the sharp coral, and shirts and shady hats to protect their skin from the melting tropical sun. Pausing to kiss, long and lingeringly—making discoveries together, not only about the reef and its secrets, but about each other.

She had never felt so happy, so exhilarated, so alive. Never in all the time she had been with Andrew had she felt this simmering excitement...this dizzying, breathless expectancy. It was wonderful, knowing that she was free at last to *feel*, that there was no longer anything to hold her back. Except—possibly—the thought of feeling too much. The thought of getting too deeply and emotionally involved. And, ultimately, getting hurt.

But she would worry about that later. She wasn't going to let anything spoil today, this weekend—nothing.

CHAPTER EIGHT

THEY arrived back at Akama Island as the sun was setting into a sea of pure gold, with just time to freshen up and change before dinner. Over pre-dinner drinks in the coolness of the air-conditioned sitting-room, Tess met Delia Branson, the woman who had raised Piers and Phoebe as her own children, for the first time.

'My dear, you look...radiant,' were the first words Dee uttered as she rose smilingly from her chair. Almost a head shorter than Tess, she was a handsome woman with greying ash-blonde hair and a fringe that almost covered her fine grey eyes. She was wearing a simple skirt and blouse and wore little make-up. This, Tess mused as she smiled back at Dee, is no plastic, peroxided, immaculately coiffed millionaire's wife. Dee looked thoroughly natural and down-to-earth. And *friendly*.

She felt her tension easing, even as she wondered if Dee was implying that her son

177

had put that radiance in her face. Would she mind if he had?

'Cruising around all day under your tropical sun, Mrs Branson, with all that breathtaking beauty to take in,' she responded with a smile, 'would be enough to make anyone feel radiant. This is my first visit to the Whitsundays,' she admitted. 'You have a very beautiful spot here.'

'Yes...' A voice spoke from behind as Julius Branson edged between them to hand Tess a drink. 'We like it here because it's private...and unspoiled.' His tone was cool. As if he were thinking, And we want to keep it that way...so this will be your first and last visit.

'Is Aunt Camille joining us for dinner, Dee?' Piers was quick to intervene, frowning at his father's coolness towards their guest.

It was Julius who answered, before Dee could speak. 'No, she's not up to it. She prefers not to come out when there are...strangers around.'

'Tess is hardly a stranger, Jules.' Piers's frown deepened. 'Didn't you tell her that Tess is a friend of mine? Tess also happens to be a doctor—and a damned good one too—so she's hardly likely to do or say anything to upset my aunt.'

Tess flicked him a surprised glance. How would he know whether she was a good doctor or not? Simply from what she'd told him herself? Or had he been checking up on her? Or... She pursed her lips. Was it just that he felt she needed someone to speak up for her? Unconsciously, she lifted her chin.

'Ah, yes...' Julius Branson's mouth took on a faintly derisive twist. 'Our guest, Dee, is a dedicated career-woman.' He made it sound like an insult.

A *career*-woman... Could that be a clue to his antagonism? Tess wondered. The fact that she'd devoted herself to a career? His wife was no career-woman. She'd given up her nursing job when she married. She was a home-body, dedicated to her family and to her various homes. Did Julius want to see his son with a similar home-body, not someone with a de-manding career of her own? Let alone—her lip twisted—a fatherless nobody from outside the Bransons' élite circle of wealthy, upper-class silvertails, with their impeccable backgrounds?

Evelyn, thankfully, chose that moment to announce that dinner was ready.

Over a delicately cooked fish meal it was Julius Branson who dominated the conversation, firing questions across the table at Piers about the family's various companies, about legal matters concerning the business, about properties the family owned and the people they knew. Piers tried to draw Tess into the conversation by throwing in topics that would be of interest to her, but it was a losing battle. Julius simply sliced in another question of his own choosing.

The one thing that made the meal bearable was the tender light in Piers's eyes every time he glanced her way, even though she knew it was inspired by desire rather than anything deeper or more meaningful. She felt it too— the same desire, hot and undeniable, flaring at the base of her stomach and quivering down to her toes.

Piers turned to ask Dee, 'Do you think Aunt Camille will feel up to it if we pop in and see her after dinner? I'd like her to meet Tess.'

'I —— ' That was as far as Dee got.

'It's too late,' Julius growled over her. 'She'll be asleep. But she did say she'd like to see you in the morning, Piers... after breakfast. Just you. She's not feeling up to meeting people, she told me. And even if she was, I wouldn't allow it. She's too weak, too easily upset. You know how frail she is.'

Once again, Tess felt like the unwanted intruder. Only Piers's comforting wink kept her spirits up. And Dee's sympathetic smile.

'The Cunninghams will be back in Australia next week,' Julius announced a moment later, and Tess was surprised when he turned to her for the first time, to explain, 'They are old friends of ours, who've been based in Europe for some years. Piers and their daughter Serena used to play together.' He snapped his gaze away to smile almost playfully at his son. 'They say she has grown into a beautiful young woman, with the loveliest disposition. But then she always was a sweet, pretty little thing. They say she's dying to meet you again, Piers, after all these years.'

Ah, Tess thought, setting her face in an impassive mask. So that's it. He has someone else in mind for Piers. That explains a lot. His hostility... It's probably nothing personal after all. I'm just the wrong girl. And he doesn't want me coming between Piers and Serena.

'Mmm . . . I remember Serena,' Piers murmured, and Tess wondered, with a tug of jealousy—a feeling she'd never experienced before meeting Piers—if that glint in his dark eyes was directed at his father, or at the memory of Serena. 'Though she was always closer to Phoebe,' he added, 'than to me.'

Julius gave a brief chuckle. 'You weren't so interested in girls in those days. It's a different story now.' His eyes slid, almost lewdly, over Tess, as if he saw her as simply the last of many like her. A bit of fluff—a brief diversion—until the right girl came along. *Serena*.

Would she see Piers again after this weekend, now that he knew Serena was coming home? It would certainly please Julius if she didn't. And how much longer would Piers be prepared to take her side, knowing how his father felt about her, knowing he wanted her out of their lives? As his father's number-one heir, just how anxious was Piers not to risk falling from favour?

She was relieved when the meal ended and Piers suggested a walk down to the beach.

After the coolness inside, the sultry heat in the garden was oppressive. Heavy, exotic scents drifted in the air as they crossed the silvery lawn to a path through the trees. Strange cackles and sharp interrogative whistles came from the branches, short staccato notes that echoed into the silence. There wasn't a breath of wind.

Piers slid an arm round her waist. 'A night made for romance...' The purr of his voice sent a deep tremor through her. 'Just look at the size of that moon.'

As Tess glanced up at the bulbous moon, suspended in a heavy, star-studded sky, she felt him draw her closer, and her pulse quickened, her heart beating suffocatingly high in her chest. The silvery wash of the moonlight guided them to the beach through tall trees and young saplings tangled with clinging, creeping vines and trailing plants. When they reached the narrow strip of pure white sand, veering to avoid a clump of boulders lying near the shore, they stood close together at the water's edge under a leaning palm, gazing out over the glass-smooth water.

The giant moon hung low in the sky, spreading a dazzling reflection on the tranquil water below.

'All we need now,' Piers breathed, his lips brushing her cheek, 'is someone strumming a guitar.'

'You should have told me,' Tess quipped. 'I'd have brought mine with me.'

'You're kidding. You play the guitar?'

'Why so surprised? I'm quite good, actually. I won it in a hospital raffle, believe it or not. An old friend—Pamela, who's brilliant at everything—taught me the basics. I find it relaxing, after a busy day. While I was studying, it helped me unwind.'

He looked down at her. 'Do you sing, too?'

'Of course.' She grinned up at him, her throat tightening as her eyes met the dark glow of his. 'How well I sing is another matter. But nobody hears me, so who cares?'

'*I'd* like to hear you.' Piers's fingers brushed over the pale skin at her nape, causing the fine hairs to prickle. 'With that deep, throaty voice of yours, I'll bet your singing voice is incredibly sexy.'

Not as incredibly sexy as you, she thought wildly, barely able to think straight as his fingers raked slowly up through her tangle of curls. With his other hand he swung her slowly round to face him. She could feel his strong thighs pressing against her legs, could feel the hard muscles of his chest crushing her breasts, could feel his hips... She felt a sharp, searing flame lick down her body.

'Piers, I——'

'I know.' Sliding his hand from her hair, he stroked his fingers across the slender line of her throat, resting them against her skin. 'Don't fight it, Tess. This is what we've both been wanting...from the moment we met.'

'It's the last thing your father would want!' The words leapt out.

Piers gave a rueful half-smile. 'When it comes to the women in my life, my father and I have seldom agreed to date.'

She felt a tiny stab of hurt. There it was again. 'The women in my life.' She was just one—the latest—of many. None of whom his father had approved, apparently.

'What about Serena?' she heard herself asking, her voice taut, despite the non-chalance she was aiming for. 'She sounds ideal for you. Your father's obviously hoping you'll end up together. Walking down the aisle.'

If he so much as hesitates, she thought, I'll know. I'll know I mean nothing to him, that I'm just a temporary distraction. A last fling, maybe.

'Not a chance.' He laughed softly. No hesitation. Her heart lifted. And then quavered. Was she being naïve? Piers was a practised rake, a past master at playing flirtatious games with women—far too smooth and sophisticated to hesitate over questions about other women. Especially when he was already aroused!

Curling his fingers under her chin, Piers tilted it gently. Then touched his mouth to hers, lightly sucking her lips. As an instant response snaked through her she summoned what strength she had left to twist her mouth away.

'You mean . . . not a chance that you'll end up walking down the aisle?' She strained for a humorous note. 'Or not a chance that you'll want Serena?'

His teeth flashed white in the moonlight. 'Mmm . . .' His voice was teasing. 'Don't tell me you're the jealous type, Tess? I never would have thought it.'

He was amused, damn him! 'I—I'm not!' she denied. Well, not normally. She never had been...until he came along. The thought shook her. Pride lifted her chin. 'I'd just like to know where I stand,' she said loftily, knowing it was a stupid, futile question. A man would tell a girl anything to get her into his bed. A man like Piers Branson more than most!

He looked down at her, his eyes black pools in the ghostly moonlight. No sign of laughter now. 'You're the one I want, Tess. Only you. Only ever you.'

Ever? She felt a tiny jolt. As his lips began trailing kisses over her cheeks, her eyes, her jaw, she felt her muscles melting, and tried to cling to sanity. How could she believe that he even knew the meaning of the word ever? But he did want her—at least for now, for the time being. And she wanted him...more than she'd ever wanted any man. And—the realisation hit her like a shock-wave—it went deeper, with her, than a purely physical need. She wanted *him*. All of him. Heart, body and soul. A girl fought for the man she wanted...

'I...feel the same,' she whispered, her need for him dragging the words out. If she lost

him, if she never saw him again... A sharp
pain pierced her at the very thought. Despite
their different backgrounds, despite their different lifestyles, they did have a lot in
common. The same humour, the same in-
tellect, many of the same interests, the same
zest for life. More, far more, than she had
ever shared with Andrew.

Yes—Piers was worth fighting for. Worth
holding on to. Even knowing his reputation,
even knowing that all he wanted from her was
her...body. Maybe he would want more—if
she could convince him that she was worth
holding on to, if she could show him a glimpse
of what he'd be missing out on, before it was
too late, before Serena came back and he
turned to her.

'Tess?'

She glanced away from him, into the
tangled bush. Somewhere on this island there
was a helicopter pilot and three crew-members
from *Mistique*. What if they'd decided to go
for a walk too? What if they decided to come
down to this beach? Even if they were nowhere about—they could, she guessed, have
gone off to one of the resort islands for the

evening—there were other precautions to think about...

She swung her gaze back to him. 'We can't just——'

'Ah...yes.' A flicker of understanding glowed in the black eyes. And possibly triumph, too? 'Never fear, my beautiful Tess...' His voice dropped to a husky whisper. 'We don't have to stay down here...' He took her face in his hands, his fingers soothing on her flushed cheeks. 'Bringing you down to the beach... Well, what better way to set the mood than a romantic stroll along a moonlit tropical beach, a lingering kiss under the stars? Besides, I thought we needed to clear the air and get away from the house, after my father's crass attempt to thrust a wedge between us. I won't let that happen, Tess. I won't let anything come between us.'

She snapped a look up at him, shaken by the savage intensity in his voice. But he was talking about now. Not letting anything come between them *now*...this weekend. What happened after that... Well, maybe that was up to her. If she wanted him enough. I do. The answer sprang from deep inside her. I do!

'Hell, Tess, if you don't want me to ravish you right here and now, don't look at me like that!'

She laughed nervously, and let her eyelashes flutter down over her cheeks. 'Is that better?' she asked, trying to inject a mocking note, but managing only a hoarse croak.

She heard his breath hiss out. His hands were still warm on her cheeks, her curls tumbling over his fingers. 'Only kisses, Tess...for now. I promise.' His lips circled her mouth, light caresses on her skin, each touch inflaming her, a sweet torture. Her lips were aching to feel his mouth on hers, but he teased her by dragging his lips away, down over the cleft of her chin, along the smooth line of her throat, into the pulsing hollow at the base.

Her breathing quickened, an intolerable hunger growing inside her with each brush of his lips. He drew back his head briefly to look down at her, then began showering kisses over her face again, over every inch of it other than her lips, still avoiding those, as if revelling in the torture he was inflicting. His own breathing was becoming more ragged, his kisses more feverish, as if he was torturing himself as much as he was her.

When his mouth finally came down on hers, her lips were parted, pouting, frantic for his kiss. Tiny moans came from her throat as he kissed her with such crushing ferocity that for a few seconds she was unable to breathe.

When he finally drew back, she was left gasping, her lips bruised and smarting. He smiled down at her, his teeth glinting tigerishly in the moonlight. 'Everyone,' he drawled thickly, 'should make love on a beach...at least once in their lifetime.'

As she stiffened, startled eyes leaping to his, he chuckled softly. 'It's all right, Tess—I don't mean now. There'll be other times, other beaches. I want this first time to feel right for you. I want you feeling free. Relaxed. No inhibitions.' He cocked his head at her. 'No regrets.'

She stared at him. Other times, he'd said. This first time. As if implying that they had a future. Or was she being naïve again? Men promised a lot of things in the heat of passion. When men like Piers Branson talked about a future, they meant an *affair*. Something they didn't intend to last...forever.

Unless she...

She drew in a deep, tremulous breath, drawing strength from deep down inside her. She hadn't fought her way to the top of her medical field without possessing a certain indomitable spirit, a determination to fight like a tiger for what she wanted. If she wanted him, she would have to make him want her as much. Or more. Make him want her, *need* her, not just once, but again and again.

She trembled, wondering what it would be like to let all her inhibitions go and abandon herself completely to a man. With Andrew, she had repressed her natural fervour, the fiery passion that simmered inside her. It had unnerved him. He had been a silent, unimaginative lover, with a conservative, almost puritan streak, more intent on controlling her sensuality than inflaming it.

She wouldn't have to repress her feelings with Piers, she suspected. Glancing up at him, she ran her tongue slowly over her lips, aware that his gaze was riveted to her mouth. If she gave full rein to the passion she felt for him . . . how would he react? She felt a shivery anticipation. Nothing like Andrew would, she had a feeling.

'It's what I want,' she breathed. 'I hope you're feeling up to it?' She raised her face provocatively to his, her eyes boldly challenging—though it was sheer bravado. Having never had a chance to explore her sexuality to the full—perhaps never having really wanted to until now—it was a little frightening. Piers had so much more experience...

His eyes seemed to darken. And then they narrowed, so that all she could see was a burning sliver of black beneath the thick black lashes. 'Let's find out...shall we?' His voice, thick with desire, sent a violent tremor through her.

With a low growl he scooped her up in his arms. Without hesitation, she wound her arms, glistening with sweat in the steamy heat, around his neck. She could feel his heart thudding against hers, as erratic as her own.

'But—what if your father sees us?' she whispered as, a few minutes later, he crashed out of the vine-clad trees and bore her across the silent, shadowy lawn surrounding the house. With his white shirt slashed open at the throat, and the muscles of his tanned arms flexing as he held her, he looked for all the world like a pirate bearing the spoils of his plunder. And *she* was the prize!

'He won't.' Piers gave a deep chuckle. 'Our bedrooms, in case you didn't notice, open out on to the veranda. No one will see us come in—no one will hear us. My parents will be at the other end of the house.'

The closer they came to the steps of the house, the more frantically her heart thudded against his, her breath quickening with each long stride he took. By the time he kicked open the door of his room and carried her inside, she felt as breathless, as feverishly impatient as he—and as certain that this was what she wanted, that *he* was what she wanted, that nothing else mattered.

It was the sound of rain that woke her, thunderous and sharp. Tess opened one eye. And saw Piers's tousled head on the pillow beside her. He was sound asleep, breathing evenly. She sat up abruptly. Dear heaven, she'd actually fallen asleep in Piers's double bed! Outside, the birds were making almost as much din as the rain. It was dawn already!

Piers stirred. 'Tess?' Without opening his eyes he reached out, his warm hand sliding over her bare skin.

Her cheeks flamed as the memory of last night flooded back in all its vivid detail. Piers undressing her, peeling off her skirt and top, and the look on his face as he had, so slowly, his hands caressingly tender, peeled off the rest, letting each item drop to the floor... Her own hands tearing at his shirt, fumbling with the buttons... Piers, getting impatient, helping her, holding her gaze all the while... The sight of his magnificent body, naked, in all its bronzed splendour, and the searing desire in his eyes as he'd looked at *her*. The touch of bare skin on bare skin, of practised hands roaming over her heated body... Gasps and moans of pleasure, of rising excitement... The sound of heavy, laboured breathing...

She realised that the heavy breathing was coming from *her*, and that it was happening now, and that the same practised hand was sliding over her bare thigh...

'It's morning!' she gasped rolling away from him and swinging her legs off the bed, away from that burning, seductive hand. 'I have to go back to my room! Where are my——?' She pounced on her denim skirt, a crumpled heap on the carpet.

Piers dragged himself up on one elbow, watching—she knew he was watching, even though she was avoiding looking at him—as she dragged on her skirt and wriggled into her black top, then snatched up her bra and panties and sandals.

'You don't have to go, you know.'

Her eyes flew to his, clashing for a second with his wicked black ones, before fluttering away, down the deeply tanned throat, down the bronzed chest, down... 'Oh, yes, I do!' She snapped her gaze away. The sight of his naked body, even partially covered by a sheet, was reminding her of sensations she had never come near to experiencing before, never believed possible. She blinked the memory, the erotic images, away. 'How can it be raining?' she cried stupidly. 'The sky was clear!'

'That was last night. The clouds don't take long to roll in at this time of year. It often rains overnight up here.' There was a thread of amusement in his voice. 'This is the wet season.'

She stole another quick glance at him. How could he sound so normal, speak so casually, when the entire earth had moved overnight? For her, at any rate. No—not only for her. There had been a time in the night when she had believed it had moved for him too. When he had cried out her name, and then whispered, not once, but over and over again, that he loved her. *Loved* her!

Were they just words, meaningless words that he was in the habit of gasping out at the height of passion? Or had he said it just to console her, because he was aware of the way she had felt? He must have been aware... Tess cringed inwardly. She had cried out herself, not only his name, not only what she was feeling, but that *she* loved *him*! And, worse, she had actually wept tears. Not tears of pain, or disappointment, but of sheer ecstasy.

'What is it, Tess? No regrets, I hope?'

Sliding a sideways look at him from under her lashes, she shook her head. 'No... it was great.' Pride kept her voice from wobbling. *Did* she have regrets? Oh, never about feeling the way she had felt, she would never have regrets about that. But... had she made a disastrous mistake, giving in to him so soon, so readily? Now that Piers had got what he wanted, now that he would no longer have the thrill of the chase to titillate him, would he begin to lose interest? Was he already losing interest, already planning to wave her goodbye once this weekend was over?

She flicked her gaze away. 'I—I'll see you at breakfast,' she mumbled, and clutching her sandals, bra and panties to her chest, she scurried to the door, thankful that her room was right next door.

She plunged straight under the shower, berating herself with each savage stroke of the soap. Why, oh, why, had she shown her feelings for him so plainly? How could she have let herself get so carried away...behaved in such a wildly uncontrolled, piteously revealing way? All that moaning and weeping, for pity's sake! Not that she'd had any control over it, but surely she could have *tried*. Her intention had been to bring Piers to his knees—not fall in a pitiable heap at his feet! Men like Piers Branson—rich, pampered playboys, who'd never been denied anything, or any*one*, in their lives—steered clear of women with feelings. They avoided emotional involvement and commitment like the plague.

They could have all the women they wanted, whenever they wanted, without it.

Oh, Tess, Tess... You have to get a man emotionally involved *before* you give in to him, you poor fool.

CHAPTER NINE

WHEN she came in to breakfast later, Piers was already there, sliding a knife through a delicately fleshed papaw. Evelyn was standing by the table, pouring tea for Julius and Dee.

She felt their eyes on her and she walked to the table with a deceptively nonchalant air, hoping she'd managed to wash off any outward trace of the torrid night before. She'd even washed her hair, which had been limp and sweaty after... She blinked away the memory.

'Good morning,' she said brightly as she pulled out a chair and sat down.

'Good morning, Tess.' There was an amused note in Piers's voice as he met her gaze across the table. And a distinct gleam in the black eyes, as if acknowledging the secret they shared. She glanced quickly away.

'I hope you slept well, Tess.' Dee smiled at her. A genuine smile, not a leer, Tess noted thankfully.

'Yes...very well, thank you.' She wasn't too surprised when the only greeting she got from Julius was a grunt, before he turned pointedly to Piers.

'Aunt Camille said she's ready to see you, son, when you've finished your breakfast. She's feeling a bit brighter this morning...and would welcome a chat, she says.'

Piers glanced at Tess. 'Then Tess can——'

'No!' Julius barked over him. 'Your aunt is still very weak—it would be too much of an effort for her, meeting someone new. You go and see her alone...and spend some time with her. Your aunt's very fond of you, you know.'

'We'll look after Tess,' Dee assured Piers. 'Tess, you might like to see the cottage garden Camille created—which I'm looking after now, of course.' She glanced out of the window. 'The rain's stopped, thank goodness. Another steamy day ahead, though, I'm afraid.'

As she spoke the sun burst through the massed clouds, its sharp rays shafting across the table, burnishing Tess's curls with vibrant Titian highlights.

'What beautiful hair you have!' Dee cried involuntarily. 'You don't often see that rich, natural red these days. You'd never believe it now,' she said, dropping her voice in a smilingly conspiratorial way, 'but Julius had red hair once, too. Before his hair turned grey, and then white more recently. His eyes were much bluer too, at one time, but they've faded too... as we all tend to fade as we get older,' she added with a sigh, fingering her own fading blonde hair.

Tess froze in her chair. Julius had once had red hair? And deeper blue eyes? Her eyes leapt to Julius Branson's face. His expression was closed, like granite. But the narrowed eyes... Hard as they were, there was something there—a faint warning?

Of course... She gulped. With his wife in the room, he wouldn't want her to say anything!

She let her lashes sweep down over her eyes. Julius was already talking about something else—discussing some business matter with Piers—she hardly took in what. She finished her breakfast in an almost breathless silence, her fingers trembling so much she could hardly hold on to anything. She was stunned, shaken, her insides churning. When she thought of last night, of the way she had given herself to Piers, hot prickles of apprehension broke out all over her skin. What had she done? She had been so sure—so sure that Julius was not her father—that there was nothing to hold her back. But now...

'I'll go and see Aunt Camille now,' Piers said, pushing back his chair.

She smiled wanly as he caught her eye, swallowing hard as he vanished through the open doorway.

Julius rose too, wincing as he straightened.

'Are you all right, dear?' Dee asked quickly.

'Of course I'm all right,' he growled. 'One has to expect a bit of discomfort after an operation.' He looked at Tess, piercing her with a hard stare. 'I'd like to see you in my study,' he said abruptly. 'You can come with me now.' He glanced at Dee. 'Put the answering machine on, will you? I don't want to be disturbed.'

Dee looked faintly puzzled, but apparently knew better than to argue with her husband. She nodded, and rose from the table to help Evelyn clear away the dishes.

'You'll find me out in the garden,' she called after them as Julius led Tess out.

Julius closed his study door behind them. Tess was dimly conscious of book-lined walls, deep leather chairs, a leather-topped desk under the window.

He didn't invite her to sit down. There was no softening in his face, now that they were out of Dee's hearing. None at all. Tess felt her spirits dip.

When Julius finally spoke, his words came as such a shock that she barely absorbed them at first.

'I want you out of my son's life. And I don't want a scene,' he warned, his tone hard as flint. 'As a doctor, you must know what that might do to my sister-in-law, in her fragile state of health. I won't have her or any of my family upset!'

Tess stared at him, her heart wrenching. He hadn't brought her in here to confess, after all this time, that he was her father, to acknowledge, even secretly, just between the two of them, that she was his daughter. He was rejecting her. And he wanted her out of his son's life as well.

Trembling, she forced her lips to part, forced her tongue to unlock. 'You're assuming an awful lot.' Her teeth were chattering so much she could barely get the words out. 'That I'm after your son. That your son wants me in his life.' She gulped, gathering strength. 'I'd say it's up to him—and me—wouldn't you?'

What was she doing? Trying to force an admission from him?

'No, I would not.' His voice was stone-hard, inflexible. 'My son is infatuated with you. It must be very flattering. I just hope it's not giving you any ideas.' His lip curled. 'He won't be satisfied until he's had you—if he hasn't already. Once he gets what he wants, he'll be on the lookout for the next conquest—the next challenge. That's his way. It always amazes me how rapidly my son's ardour cools once he's had his way with a woman.'

Tess lifted a defiant chin, hiding the misery she felt inside. He was only telling her what she knew already. Hadn't Piers himself warned her not to expect a 'meaningful relationship'?

Turning away from her, Julius picked up something from the desk.

'I want you to have this,' he said, and for the first time Tess detected a faint note of sympathy in his voice. Or *pity*. 'I don't expect you to go away empty-handed,' he growled. 'My son has no doubt given you certain...expectations, unconsciously or otherwise. Expectations he has no intention of fulfilling.' He thrust out his hand. 'Once you accept this, you're out of our lives...for good. You understand? Refuse to accept it—and you'll get nothing. Ever. Here...' He pushed it into her hand. 'Take it...and go. The helicopter's waiting outside, ready to take you to the airport.'

Her heart plunging, she glanced down. It was a cheque. She recoiled in shock when the figure leapt at her.

'You're offering me *five hundred thousand dollars*?' she croaked, gaping at the cheque, and then jerking a look up at him. She whispered painfully, 'You'd offer me half a million dollars...to get rid of me?' Inside, she could feel her heart splintering into thousands of tiny pieces.

'To get out of my son's life, yes.' He was like a statue, as immovable and unfeeling as rock. 'I think it should go a good way towards softening the blow of parting—don't you agree?'

She looked into his face, saw no wavering, and felt desolation wash over her. From somewhere, perhaps from her years of facing pain and distress as a doctor, she found the strength to speak, seizing what she saw as her last chance to draw the truth from him.

'You don't need to buy my silence, Mr Branson,' she said dully. 'I have no intention of telling anyone your secret, or of making any claim on you or your family, or—or causing any trouble. I...just wanted to—to know if it was true. So that I could thank you for what you've done for my mother and me all these years.'

A heavy, ghastly silence fell between them. Julius seemed to swell as she watched. And then he doubled over in pain.

'Mr Branson!' she cried in alarm, letting the cheque flutter from her fingers as she rushed to him. 'Please...you must sit down!' She led him to a chair, eased him into it. 'I— I didn't mean to distress you.'

'Distress me?' Scorn lashed his voice. He shook off her hand, his expression savage as he glared up at her. 'I'm not distressed—I'm *outraged*. Just what the hell do you think you're accusing me of?'

'I—I didn't mean to sound accusing, Mr Branson...far from it!' she was quick to reassure him. 'I just...' She gulped. 'All I wanted was to—to meet you. To know who m-my father was. I...' She faltered, her heart quailing when she saw the black fury, the rejection in his face.

'Your *father*?' he roared, his withering tone lashing her.

She flinched. Was he denying it? Her eyes narrowed as she looked at him more closely, her shoulders slumping as realisation hit her.

'You never cared about my mother at all!' she choked out. 'You didn't send her money because you cared about her...or about me. It was simply to buy her silence! The way you've been trying to buy mine ever since she died! And n-now you're trying to buy me off, shut me up, once and for all...with a small fortune!' Hot tears sprang to her eyes, and she angrily dashed them away. 'You never cared for either of us! You just wanted to brush us under the carpet—out of sight. Out of your life!' She pointed a quivering finger at the cheque on the floor. 'And I suppose you're trying to appease your conscience as——'

'Stop it!' he slashed over her. 'I don't know where the hell you got this monstrous idea, but you couldn't be more wrong! *I am not your father*! If your mother told you I was, she was lying! If I'd been able to have children, I would have had them with my wife, not with my married secretary!'

The blood seeped from her cheeks. 'If...you'd been *able* to have children?' she echoed hoarsely.

His lips drew into a thin white line. 'I'm infertile,' he bit out baldly. 'Why do you think my wife and I adopted Piers and Phoebe and had no other children? Because we couldn't have children of our own! Because *I* couldn't!'

Tess sagged where she stood, wishing the floor would open up and swallow her. 'I—I thought it was your wife who——'

'Well, you were wrong! Do I have to call her in to convince you? Do I have to show you my test results? Call in a doctor?'

She shook her head in abject misery. 'I—I'm sorry,' she mumbled. 'I thought——'

'Well, you thought wrong! And if you ever repeat any thoughts like that outside this room, I'll destroy you! And don't think I can't do it!'

She rallied momentarily, lifting pained eyes to his. 'Are you threatening me, Mr Branson?'

'You'll find out if you spread lies like that around!'

Lies... Oh, my God, she thought, what have I done? She bowed her head. 'I won't—of course I won't,' she assured him miserably. 'I—I just didn't know who else it could be. Who else would have had the means to be so...generous.'

Julius made a dismissive gesture. 'Your mother often travelled with me—she could have met anyone. We weren't together all the time, you know. And certainly *never* overnight!'

Her head jerked back, hope flaring in her eyes. 'You—you know of someone?'

'No.' An implacable no. 'All I know is that it wasn't me.' He stabbed her with his hard gaze. 'You're to promise me that you won't breathe a word of what you've said in this room to anyone. *Anyone*—you understand?'

'I won't,' she whispered. She could understand his not wanting rumours of that nature flying around, even if he could prove they weren't true. Rumours tended to persist, regardless of the truth. People could get hurt. His family, his reputation, even his business . . .

'I won't bother your family again,' she promised, her heart twisting as she thought of Piers. Julius would explain to him why she had gone—and Piers, knowing that she had used him, that she had sought his friendship solely to get access to his father, would be glad to see the last of her. His interest in her was probably fading already, now that she'd given him what he wanted . . .

'Now . . . go,' Julius said wearily. 'I'd like to rest. Take the cheque, collect your things, and go. *Now*. And go quietly.' He let his head slump on to his chest. 'I want you out of our lives!'

She swayed for a moment in front of him. Yes—it was best that she left quickly and quietly. Without seeing anyone. Without causing any more trouble, any more distress.

Without waiting around to be hurt and humiliated by Piers's rejection as well.

'Keep your money, Mr Branson,' she breathed, clenching her fists in a flare of angry resentment as it struck her that the money had had nothing to do with buying her silence— he had simply wanted to buy her *off*, to get her out of his son's life. She wasn't suitable. She wasn't one of *them*. She was a nobody. A nobody who didn't even know who her father was, who went around making wild accusations!

'I'm leaving.' She turned stiffly away. 'No need to fear that I'll make a scene...' Did he think her so insensitive that she would kick up a fuss, knowing there was a frail, terminally ill woman in the house? Or that she would go running to Piers for support, and risk tearing his family apart? 'I'll be gone before anyone even knows I've left. Goodbye, Mr Branson.'

She stumbled from the room. Five minutes later she was gazing out of the window of the helicopter as the house she'd left behind grew smaller and smaller below, the palm-trees bowed by the down-draught of the propeller, the surrounding lawns a brilliant green after the overnight rain. Nobody ran from the house. Nobody appeared at the doors or windows. Nothing so much as moved.

She hadn't seen Piers before she left. He had been still closeted with his aunt. Delia was somewhere in her garden, on the other side of the house.

Julius Branson had his wish. She was out of their lives.

The first thing she did when she got back to Sydney, apart from throwing herself back into her work to try to forget Piers, was to visit her family lawyer and demand the name of the man who had been sending money to her and her mother all these years. Her lawyer, a rather pompous, ambitious young man who had taken over from her mother's original lawyer, told her that he was acting under a strict code of secrecy and that it would be more than his life was worth—his *reputation*, he meant—to reveal the man's identity. He didn't deal with the man directly, he stiffly informed her, he dealt only through the 'other party's' lawyers. Tess wondered if perhaps he was unaware himself who the 'other party' was.

'Well, you can get in touch with your "other party's" lawyers,' she commanded with steely determination, 'and get them to inform this man, whoever he is, that I won't accept any more of his money. Ever. So he can stop sending it. As of now. If you hand me a pen, I'll put that in writing.'

The young man looked startled. 'Are you sure?'

'Quite sure.' It was obvious that her father didn't want to know her, had no wish to meet her. He was never going to acknowledge, even in private, that he was her father. He was only doing what he thought was his duty. Out of a sense of obligation, not love. She didn't *need* that. Or want it.

As she signed the necessary document she felt no regret. She wanted no more of her father's conscience money, or his charity, or whatever it was. She wanted no further connection with him. She didn't even care any more who he was. All she cared about... But she wasn't going to think about Piers either. That chapter in her life was closed. Finished.

Four weeks dragged by. It felt more like four months. Life went on, but there was no joy in it. She kept seeing Piers's face, in her mind, in her dreams, in every crowd... She kept thinking of things she wanted to tell him, or laugh over with him, or discuss with him. Worst were the memories. Memories of his arms around her, his mouth hungry on hers, his hands stroking her body to passionate life, their naked bodies fusing... But she knew it was futile to keep on clinging to thoughts of him. Piers wasn't going to come.

For the first few days and weeks she had foolishly clung to the dim hope that he would suddenly appear on her doorstep, that his feelings for her had been deeper, stronger than she had imagined, and that he had decided to put them ahead of his hurt and forgive her for the way she had used him. For days, weeks, she'd clutched at the hope that he would defy his father and tell him to his face that he loved her, despite what she had done, and that he was going to her whether he liked it or not.

But he didn't come—either that first week, or the next, or the next—and she threw herself even deeper into her work in an attempt to piece herself together and become whole again.

One Sunday evening around dusk, when she heard a knock at her front door and saw the back of a man's head in shadowy outline through the spyhole in the door, she clutched her chest, thinking he had finally come. She took a moment to compose herself, though she was incapable of calming her wildly thumping heart. She glanced round help-lessly, wishing there was time to touch up her lipstick, brush her hair, change into a clean shirt.

When another rap came, she sighed, and pulled open the door.

'Andrew!' She sagged in disappointment. 'H-hello.'

She hadn't seen him for weeks, had barely even spared him a thought.

'May I come in?' he asked, his tone dif-fident, his hazel eyes wary.

She nodded and stepped back. 'Coffee?' she asked as she waved him inside.

'No, thanks. Just called in to see how you are.' The eyes that ran over her face had a gratified glint, she thought. 'You look a bit wan, Tess. Not sleeping well?'

She gave him a narrowed look. 'If you have something to say, Andrew, spit it out. I'm not in the mood for your games. I never was, if you remember.'

'No...I can imagine that you wouldn't be in the mood for frivolity at the moment. I hear that you and Piers Branson have split up.' He eyed her in mock sympathy. 'My commiserations.'

Her knuckles whitened—her only outward reaction. 'If you're thinking that the way's clear now, Andrew, for *you*...'

He compressed his lips, a touch of colour staining his sallow cheekbones. 'Hardly.' He thrust out his jaw, his lip lifting in disdain. 'We don't seem to have much in common any more, do we? In fact...I'm seeing someone else.' He paused, eyeing her expectantly.

Not wanting to disappoint him, she asked, without really caring, 'Someone I know?'

'It is, as a matter of fact. It's your friend Pamela.'

Now he *had* surprised her! 'Well...I wish you both all the best,' she said, wondering if that was why Pamela had looked a trifle apprehensive the other day when they'd bumped into each other. Was she afraid, as an old friend, that she might be encroaching?

Pamela knew, of course, that Piers was no longer in the picture.

'Did she suggest this...visit?' Tess asked slowly. Had Pamela wanted to give them a final chance to make up? To make sure that the way was clear before she got more deeply involved with Andrew?

Andrew shrugged. 'Well...partly.'

'And the other part?'

The two spots of colour deepened. 'I wanted to see you anyway. I thought there was something you ought to know...'

She raised her brows, steeling herself inside. 'Well?'

'Pamela and I saw Piers Branson at the theatre last night. He was there with Serena Cunningham. They looked very happy and at ease together.' He paused to let that sink in. 'They say Julius Branson is all in favour of the match. The Bransons and the Cunninghams are old friends...' He pursed his lips, a smug gleam in his eyes. 'The word's going round that Piers has stopped sowing his wild oats at long last and is ready to settle down.'

She felt the room tilt. Sheer strength of will kept her standing. Somehow she found her voice. 'And you thought I should know.'

'Tess, until we saw Piers with Serena last night, we thought that you and he might... Well, that you could be holding on to the hope that you and he might still get back together. But after seeing him with Serena...'

'You decided I should be told so that I didn't cling to any futile hopes.' She drew in a fractured breath. 'You can tell Pamela, Andrew, that I'm not holding a torch for Piers *or* for you. You and she—you have my blessing, OK?' She moved woodenly to the door. 'Since you won't have coffee, Andrew, and I have a lot to do...'

He nodded, shrugging. 'I'm sorry he got away, Tess.' He wasn't quite able to repress the gloating light in his eye. 'He would have been quite a catch. But I did warn you...'

She squeezed her hands into tight fists, her nails digging into her palms. 'Yes, you did warn me. Goodbye, Andrew.'

'Goodbye, Tess.' He touched her arm as he stepped past her. 'Better luck next time, eh? Try steering clear of playboy tycoons from now on—they live in another world, Tess.'

With a supreme effort she managed not to slam the door behind him, determined not to give him the satisfaction. But the moment he'd gone she snatched up a cushion from the sofa and began banging it down on an armchair, again and again, with all the strength left in her body.

CHAPTER TEN

THE following Saturday Tess was strumming on her guitar in a desultory fashion, trying to cheer herself up before summoning the energy to make herself an omelette for dinner, when the doorbell rang. She put down the guitar with a sigh, hoping it wasn't Andrew and Pamela. She wasn't in the mood. Not that she wasn't happy for them both   she truly wished them well, and had already told Pamela so on the phone. It was just that she wasn't feeling terribly sociable at the moment, and hadn't been for the past week.

She opened the door without bothering to look through the spyhole. And froze, her hand clutching the door-knob for support.

'Hello, Tess.'

For a breathless moment all she could do was stare at him. He looked no different. The same quirking eyebrow, the same wry tilt of the lips, the same spikes of dark hair across his brow, the same wicked black... No, his eyes *were* different somehow—she wasn't sure how.

'What are you doing here?' she managed finally, her voice a husky whisper.

'I just came to see how you were, Tess.' His expression was as impassive as his tone, his eyes equally unreadable. 'I was surprised to find you at home actually...on a Saturday evening. I thought you'd have been out on the town—living it up.' Now there was a faintly derisive edge to his voice.

She thought of Serena, and of the weeks that had gone by without her hearing a word from him, and she lifted her chin. 'I'm surprised to see *you*...on a Saturday evening,' she retorted, holding herself together with an effort. 'Did you come alone, or is Serena with you?' she glanced past him, as if expecting to see her in his car out at the front.

'Serena?' His eyes pierced hers, black and unfathomable. 'When you walked out on me Tess, without a word, I imagined that I was free to take out whomever I pleased.'

She hid a stab of hurt. He was implying that she'd walked away without any thought for him. 'Of course,' she conceded with a shrug, her pale face taut. He hadn't wasted any time finding someone else. If he'd cared about her he would have come after her weeks ago. But he hadn't. Why had he come now?

The black eyes searched her face. 'You look tired, Tess. Pale. You're thinner, too.' His mouth took on a mocking tilt. 'Too many late nights?'

She gave a brief laugh. 'Think that, if you like.' Too many sleepless nights, more like, tossing morosely in her bed. Peering at him more closely, she realised that there were subtle changes in his face, too. New lines round his mouth, faint smudges under his eyes, and the usually lively black eyes ... Yes, she knew what it was now. Hooded as they were, all the old humour, all the life, the light, had gone from them. Had he been having too many late nights himself? With Serena? Or was it because he was here with *her*. He'd probably never had a girl walk out on him before, and he didn't like it!

His brow plunged under her scrutiny. 'I wasn't even sure you'd still be here,' he said roughly.

Her eyes flicked wider. 'And just where did you think I would be?'

His shoulders lifted and fell. 'I thought you would have been living in more luxury by now. Or might already have scooted off overseas for a glamorous extended holiday—first class all the way, of course.'

She squinted at him. 'What the hell are you talking about?'

He glanced round at the car parked in her car-port. 'Still the same old Ford—I thought you'd have had a more swanky model by now.' His eyes raked down her body, over her old faded jeans and loose shirt. 'And where's the new finery? The expensive hair-do? The diamond ear-rings?' He seized her wrist. 'Not even a new watch!'

He dropped her hand and pushed past her, striding into her living-room. 'Not even a new stick of furniture! Not even a new painting or a Lalique crystal figurine!' He spun round, and in one long stride stood over her, his hands grasping her by the shoulders. 'What's going on, Tess? What have you done with all the money?'

'All the —— ?' Her face turned pale as light finally dawned. 'You think...' She flicked an angry tongue over her lips. 'You mean, your father told you I'd *accepted* that money he offered me?'

Piers went deathly still. He stared at her. Then he sucked in a deep, quivering breath. 'Bloody...hell!' he grated. 'No—not in so many words. But he let me think it. He told me he'd offered you a small fortune—to find out if all you were after was our money.' His mouth twisted in disgust. She wondered if it was directed at his father or at her. 'Then he told me you'd gone—that you'd both decided it best that you left quickly and quietly, without saying goodbye. Naturally, I assumed...'

Tess sagged, and only the hands gripping her kept her upright. 'Wh-what else did your father tell you?' she whispered.

'Nothing. Why? Was there more?' he asked, piercing her with a laser-sharp look.

Her lips parted. Just in time, she remembered her promise to Julius not to breathe a word to anyone about the accusation she had made. *Nobody*, he had stressed. Since it was obvious he hadn't told Piers, that meant him too. Whether Julius was concerned about the distress it might cause within his own family, the doubts it could raise in their minds, or that it might leak out, leading to rumours on a wider scale, the result would be the same. His family, especially Dee, could be hurt, his own reputation tarnished.

She shook her head, her heart shrivelling inside. 'If you thought I'd accepted your father's money,' she choked out, 'why did you come to see me? To abuse me?'

Piers drew in his lips, his hands tightening their grip on her shoulders, jerking her closer. 'Damn it, why do you think I came? Because I couldn't stay away from you any longer! Because I still wanted you, and didn't care if you'd accepted his damned money or not! I was prepared to offer you *more*—whatever you wanted—if that was the only way I could have you!'

She caught her breath, staring up at him dazedly. He was saying he still wanted her? That he'd wanted her even when he'd believed that she had been after him for his money? Even when he'd believed that she had accepted his father's money? She felt a piercing pain that he could have believed such a thing of her.

'I thought you knew me better,' she breathed painfully. 'Thought more of me.' He knew her no better than Andrew did!

A shadow crossed his face. 'You were the one who put the doubts in my head, Tess,' he said heavily. 'All those questions you asked—about my father, about the family business, about our homes, our lives... and whether I intended to give up the law, as if you were scared I was thinking of throwing away my inheritance. And then when Julius told me he'd offered you all that money and you'd *gone*...' He gave a shuddering sigh. 'What else did you expect me to think?'

His sigh echoed in her own heart. Yes—she could see it now. If he'd had doubts about her, if he'd thought her a gold-digger, she had no one to blame but herself. Her intense interest in Julius Branson must have seemed... suspect, to say the least.

His fingers were biting into her arms. 'If you didn't accept that money, Tess, why did you run away? Why didn't you come to me?' His eyes probed hers, a tiny flame glowing in the black depths. 'Because you thought I might have been in on it? That I might have wanted to find out, as much as my father did, if you could be bought off?'

'No!' she gasped. 'I never thought that!'

'Well, then...*why*, Tess? Because you felt so hurt and insulted that all you wanted was to get away from all of us?'

She dropped her gaze under his. Better that he should believe that than have him trying to draw the truth from her. And it was close enough to the truth, after all.

But he still wasn't satisfied. 'Or were you *afraid* to tell me,' he asked slowly, 'because you thought I'd raise hell on your behalf and a row might upset my aunt? Julius no doubt having warned you,' he added through tight lips, 'that you could have her death on your conscience if you caused any trouble?'

'Piers...does it matter?' she said, with a trembling sigh.

'Yes, it damned well does,' he ground out. 'I thought you and I had something going, Tess. I would have sworn you felt the way I do. If you didn't, you certainly fooled me that night we spent together...'

'D-Don't, Piers,' she pleaded, leaning back, trying to twist her face away from his. His warm breath and the sensuous lips she'd dreamed about night after night were so tantalisingly close they were fuzzing her brain.

He gave her a shake. 'Why didn't you come to me later on, Tess, after I got back,' he grated, 'and at least try to thrash things out?'

She shrugged, her lashes sweeping down to avoid his relentless gaze. 'What was the point? It wasn't as if you and I were...' she faltered, then mumbled with a sigh, 'Piers, we had our fun. We had some good times together. Let's just leave it at that.'

'So that's all it was to you, Tess? Just a bit of fun. Some good times... with a taste of the high life thrown in!' His tone was scathing. 'You always wanted to visit a tropical island, you said. So—now you have.' His eyes hardened. 'You've had your fun and that's it, is it?'

She bit back the denial on her lips. Better to let him go on thinking that was all it had been to her. She'd be a fool to think he wanted her as a permanent fixture in his life, to have any illusions about a long-term future with him. He'd said a minute ago that he still wanted her. *Wanted*, not loved. Loving would be for someone like Serena. Someone suitable. Someone born to a similar lifestyle, who would bask in his family's approval. Someone he could marry and have children with—children with impeccable, *known* backgrounds.

She drew in a deep, tremulous breath. 'What is it you want from me, Piers?' she asked painfully. 'A last little fling, before you settle down with Serena? Or do you plan on going on having flings *after* you marry her? Buying any woman you happen to fancy!'

He frowned. 'Marry Serena? Is that what you think I'm planning to do?'

When all she could do was shake her head, he dug his fingers more savagely into her arms. 'Tess, I've known Serena for years. She's a great girl. Since she's been back in Australia I've taken her out a couple of times. Just to dinner, to a show. Maybe I hoped I *would* feel something for her. But I didn't, Tess. And do you know why? Because I kept seeing *your* face, kept looking around for *you*, wanting *you* with me.' He lashed an arm round her waist, pinning her body to his, his black eyes glittering into hers. 'You're the one I want in my life, Tess—in my arms, in my bed—not Serena.'

She felt her body stirring, weakening, urging her to melt against the strong muscles of his chest, to feel her body moulding into his, into the hard thighs, the straining hips. She longed to feel more of the sensations she'd been dreaming of ever since that breathtaking night.

'And you want me, Tess,' he breathed, his lips an aching breath from hers. 'You think I don't know, can't feel it? We belong together, Tess...'

'Belong?' she echoed above the wild beat of her heart. 'That sounds odd—coming from a man who once warned me not to expect a meaningful relationship...'

He swore softly. 'When I said that, Tess, I'd only just met you. I...wasn't sure what you wanted,' he admitted. 'You seemed more interested in the Branson *family* than in me— in the Branson wealth, I imagined at the time. I thought if it was only my money you were after, maybe if I warned you that you had no hope of getting it, you might—well, have second thoughts about getting tangled up with me. A man has to protect himself against predatory females,' he said, his eyes showing a spark of his old humour.

'If you thought I was a predatory female,' she breathed, 'why did you go on seeing me?'

'Ah . . . good question. Why do men do the things they do? Why do they make fools of themselves over women? I guess I'm not the first . . .'

'You're no fool, Piers Branson,' she murmured. 'A barrister as talented as you doesn't go around making a fool of himself.'

His eyes held hers, a yellow flame kindling in the black. 'Any man, Tess, can make a fool of himself over a woman. If the woman means enough to him.' His voice roughened. 'Hell, Tess, if you only knew!' Jerking her closer, he buried his face in the warm hollow beneath her jaw. 'All the time I was chasing after you,' he dragged out, his voice muffled against her skin, 'I wasn't sure, in the beginning, if I was trying to get you out of my system . . . or trying to blot out the doubts I had about getting more involved with you—a girl I wasn't sure wanted me for myself! And when my father told me you'd gone—and let me believe that you'd accepted his money—a small fortune . . .'

'It confirmed what you'd suspected,' she said softly. 'It made you go on believing the worst of me.'

He raised his head and looked deep into her eyes. 'I came to you, didn't I—even believing the worst of you? I must have known in my heart it wasn't true . . . But even if it had been, it wouldn't have mattered. I want you, Tess. When I told you that night we made love that I loved you, I wasn't just mouthing meaningless platitudes . . . or getting carried away in the heat of passion. I meant it. I still mean it. I love you, Tess. I'll always love you.'

A tremor of disbelief, of wonder, shook through her. She felt her defences crumble. 'Oh, Piers, I've been so miserable,' she moaned, tears glistening on the tips of her lashes. 'There hasn't been a moment when I haven't longed for you.'

'No more miserable than I've been.' His hand slid through her hair, his fingers clutching at her curls, tilting her head back. 'We were meant for each other, Tess . . . We belong together . . .'

As an exquisite, almost painful sweetness flooded her body at the words he brought his mouth down on hers, and the weeks they'd been apart slid away as if they'd never been.

If their lovemaking the first time had been wild and abandoned, it was a conflagration this time—so intense, so quickly reaching the heights, that there was no time or thought for tender foreplay or leisurely exploration. They were both moaning aloud, crying out their love for each other, as they spun to the heights of ecstasy together, reeling into a world where nothing mattered, nothing hurt, nothing else existed but each other, and wave after wave of throbbing pleasure...until finally they felt themselves floating away, drifting into an endless, euphoric plateau of wonder and peace.

They made love over and over again throughout that long, rapturous night, more leisurely love each time, more satisfying, deeper, exploring every sensitive zone of each other's bodies, dwelling, in exquisite pleasure, on each new sensation, each piquant revelation. And in between they slept, wrapped in each other's arms.

The next day, Sunday, they didn't leave Tess's house, barely moving from her bed, passion flaring between them again and again.

It was as if they couldn't have enough of each other, couldn't keep their hands off each other.

In the slumbrous moments in between, they talked.

'I've been very remiss,' Tess said as she lay curled in his arms on the sofa, drinking hot soup from a mug. 'I haven't asked how your aunt is.'

'Aunt Camille?' Piers kissed the tip of her nose. 'She's still hanging in there—she's amazing. But it's only a matter of time. I've already said goodbye to her, in case I'm not there when the time comes.'

'And...your father?' Tess asked tentatively. 'He's recovering well?'

'He's back at work. Back here in Sydney— during the week, at any rate. He flies back to the island each weekend. My mother's staying up there all the time just now, to be with Aunt Camille.'

'Your mother's a fine person, Piers,' Tess said with feeling.

'I agree. She already has a soft spot for you.'

Tess bit her lip, her eyes pained. 'I left without even saying goodbye to her.'

'She'll understand...when she knows what Julius did to you. If she doesn't know already. She's probably already given him the rounds of the kitchen. Shh...' He hushed her as she seemed about to say something. 'Don't let's talk...' He plucked her empty mug from her fingers and put it down on the floor, then nuzzled his face in her hair, his tongue making an erotic exploration of the sensitive folds of her ear. Sudden heat blazed between them, and they tore off the towels they'd wrapped round themselves and made love again right there, rolling off the sofa on to the carpet.

As they lay, sated for the time being, in each other's arms Tess warned him soberly, 'Your father won't be happy about this. He doesn't want you to have anything to do with me.'

Piers stroked her face. 'When my father knows you the way I do, he'll love you too,' he said unworriedly. 'He must already be squirming about what he did to you. I'm sure it's done him the world of good, having his disgusting offer thrown back in his face. I'd like to——'

'No, Piers!' She pressed a finger to his lips. 'Please...let it be.' She was the one who'd offered the greater insult, wrongly accusing

Julius of being her father—of being the man who had made her mother pregnant. 'I'm sure he was only trying to—to protect you. To protect his family.'

'Well, serve him right if he is squirming,' Piers growled, 'for making the mistake of thinking you were a money-hungry little gold-digger.'

She sighed. 'When he knows we're back together, he'll be sure of it,' she said sombrely. 'He'll say I was only holding out for more. For what I can get out of *you*.'

Piers gave a low chuckle. 'If you were, you'd hardly be pointing that out to me. Before you even have a ring on your finger.'

Her eyes flew to his. 'A—a ring?'

He untangled himself from her arms and lifted her on to the sofa, dropping to his knees at her feet. 'My darling, Tess...' He caught her hand. 'You weren't imagining, I hope, that I had no intention of making an honest woman of you? I *love* you. And I intend to marry you. I'm asking you to marry me. Will you marry me?'

It came as such a shock that only the fact that she was sitting already saved her from toppling over.

'Piers...do you know what you're saying?' She searched his face—a face already so dear to her. 'I didn't think you were into commitment. Let alone——'

'I wasn't,' he cut in blithely. 'Until I met you. You've changed everything for me, Tess. Now I know what loving a woman means. You're the one. The only one. You'll only ever be the one. So why should we wait? I want to announce our engagement and let the world know.'

She shook her head dazedly. 'I... Piers, isn't it a bit soon?' she whispered. 'Marriage is an enormous step. It means...for life. Or it does in my book.'

'Mine too. Which is why I've never proposed to anyone before. And I never intend to again. For me, this is it. I *know*, Tess, how I feel. I don't need to wait.' The glittering black eyes—more tender now than wicked— searched hers. 'I did hope...it might be the same for you.'

She gulped. 'It—it's happening too fast.' Was it only a day ago that she had despaired of ever seeing him again? 'You and I... Piers, there are so many differences between us— our lifestyles...'

He gave a snort. 'I haven't noticed any differences. We both like the same things, as far as I'm aware. And if the Branson wealth leaves you cold, as you insist it does——'

'You don't call that a difference?' she broke in with a sigh. 'You're used to it. I'm not. I'd be embarrassed to have all that wealth—to have people fawning over me because of it. To see people who didn't have it—and yet needed it more.' She flushed. 'There. You see? It will never work. I'd feel uncomfortable in your world...'

'Stop talking about my world, as if we both live on different planets. As I started to say before—now that I know my money isn't of any interest to you, you won't mind, presumably, if I give it all up?'

She gaped at him. 'Give it up? How? What do you mean?'

He chuckled softly. 'If you could see your face, Tess! A lot of women would have been looking horrified—dismayed. They'd be accusing me of being mad. Your eyes, on the other hand, Tess, lit up. With what looks suspiciously like hope!'

She gave a wary smile. 'Are you saying... you intend to devote yourself solely to being a barrister, Picrs, and not take over your father's business?'

'You wouldn't mind?'

'No! Of course not! I was appalled that you were even considering it.'

'I wasn't, actually,' he said with a sheepish grin. 'I just let you think so. Because at the time, my darling, I thought you *would* mind if I did. If I recall, I told you I couldn't do both. So I didn't actually lie. I didn't want to risk losing you, you see. And I thought I might if I told you outright that I had no intention of taking control of my father's media empire when the time comes.'

'Oh, Piers.' In a way, he had been as devious as she! If she hadn't had her mind set on meeting Julius Branson, she might have let her scruples overcome her and turned her back on Piers then and there! Reminded of Julius, she asked warily, 'How does your father feel about this decision of yours?'

'He doesn't believe I mean it. He's still hoping I'll change my mind. That's why he insists I spend at least some of my time in the business, getting familiar with the various organisations. I don't mind that, because I'll still be prepared to do legal work on behalf of the company. And I'm happy to remain a director. I just won't be an *executive* director. *The* executive director.'

'So...who'll run the companies, if you don't?' Tess asked curiously. She could imagine how devastated Julius would be when he realised Piers was serious.

'Phoebe and Tom. They already have senior positions in the company. And Phoebe's doing brilliantly. She's very suited to it. Julius can't see it—yet—because he's used to wives being at home, and staying in the background. But Dee thrives on that life. Phoebe's different. She's a born career-woman. Domesticity leaves her cold. She and Tom don't even want children.'

He caught her hand and pressed it to his cheek. 'But you're diverting me. Here I am, down on my knees to you—fast getting housemaid's knee!—and we're discussing business. Tess...I mean it. I want to marry you. I love you. And you love me.' The wicked sparkle danced back into his eyes. 'You've already told me so—not once, but again and again. You're not going to tell me it was the heat of the moment that made you say it...or that you didn't realise what you were saying at the time?'

'Oh, I realised it.' She smiled tenderly into his eyes. 'And...I meant it,' she confessed, almost shyly. 'They say when you really love someone you know. With Andrew I...' She hesitated, but his eyes encouraged her to go on. 'I couldn't make a serious commitment because I wasn't sure...and the longer we were together, the less sure I became. I did love him, but... Well, maybe I just thought I did. With you, Piers...I *know*,' she said simply.

The love that blazed from his eyes sent a deep happiness quivering through her. 'Well, then...' A smile curved his lips—an irresistible, lopsided, sensuous smile. 'Love and marriage go together, I always thought. Tess, if you love me, say yes. Put me out of my misery. Then let's announce our engagement and let everyone know.'

Her eyes shone. Then wavered. 'You mean...let your father know. Piers—I'm not sure.'

'Not sure about me?'

'No!' She shook her head vehemently.

'Then what is it? You're not hesitating because you think my father will...disapprove?' he asked, frowning. 'What are you afraid of, Tess? That he'll say you jumped at the offer? Accuse you of catching me at a vulnerable moment, after all those weeks apart?'

Her eyelashes swept down. He knew her too well already! 'I would like to know I have your parents' blessing. Piers...' She looked up at him. 'Let's wait for a week...at least,' she pleaded, 'before we talk marriage.'

'You're right,' he said suddenly, surprising her. 'You need more wooing. More courting time. More time just for the two of us. Before everyone gets to know how I feel about you.'

She smiled, shivering in anticipation. 'That sounds wonderful. But I meant——'

'You meant you want more time for us to get to know each other.' He ran his eyes hungrily over her, as if what he knew about her already was enough for him.

She blushed, and nodded. What she wanted was to give *him* some breathing space—some more time to think about what he was doing, and whether he would be prepared to defy his father, if necessary. To be sure that *he* was sure. She knew *she* was. She had never been more sure of anything in her life.

'That's what engagements are for, Tess.' He touched a tender hand to her cheek. 'For two people, already committed to each other, to get to know each other better. But OK...I'll give you a week. One week before I pop the question again. And next time I'll expect you to say yes.'

CHAPTER ELEVEN

A WEEK later, to the day, Piers proposed again, and this time Tess accepted without hesitation, Piers having shown her, in hundreds of different ways, that he'd meant every word he'd said the previous Sunday.

At lunchtime the next day they met at an exclusive antique jeweller's shop to choose a ring.

'What about this one?' Piers picked out a dazzling diamond solitaire, set in a heavily embossed gold band.

Tess shook her head. 'Too big. I'd snag it in everything. I'd like a ring I can wear all the time... and feel comfortable wearing.'

'How about a sapphire—to match your eyes?'

'Mmm...yes, I like sapphires.' She held up a pale hand. 'A sapphire would give my skin a bit of colour.'

'Your hair and eyes, Tess, and those delicious lips of yours, already give you as much colour as you'll ever need.' Piers brushed a light hand over her bright Titian curls.

She blushed, her heart swelling with sheer happiness. The past few days wiped out all the preceding weeks of pain and misery as if they had never been—each day, even if they'd only had time to meet for lunch, bringing new discoveries, revealing new things about him to love and admire, each night transporting her to wondrous new heights.

'I like this one.' She held it up—a neat square sapphire, as brilliantly blue as her own eyes, embedded in a nest of tiny diamonds.

'Very you,' Piers said approvingly. 'Beautiful...and tasteful. And it has a wedding-ring to go with it, with the same intertwined gold band. Here...let me put it on for you.'

As he slipped it on to her finger—a perfect fit!—she trembled with emotion, her mind leaping ahead to their wedding-day when he would slip the matching ring on her finger. But with it came a swift qualm.

'I wouldn't like to get married, Piers, without your father's blessing,' she blurted out.

'No problem.' Piers dismissed her concern. 'I spoke to him again this morning—he's on Akama. I told him that I was going to ask you today—for the second time—to marry me. That I loved you and intended to go on asking you to marry me until you agreed. He accepts it, Tess. He won't stand in our way.'

'Accepts it . . . but isn't happy about it.' She felt a twinge of regret. He would be her father-in-law, the nearest thing to a father that she had ever had. And he would never be happy about having her as a daughter. He'd be hoping they broke up before the wedding. He'd be doing his subtle best to make sure they did. So that the more acceptable Serena, no doubt, could catch Piers on the rebound.

'If he wasn't happy about it, my love, he'd hardly be offering us the use of *Mistique* for our engagement party.'

'He has?' Her eyes brightened, then clouded. 'But he won't be there . . . ?' She knew that Piers had already confronted Julius about his heavy-handed attempt to buy her off, and for giving the impression that she'd taken the money and run. Julius, according to Piers, had defended his stand without shame or apology, declaring that it had been a test for Piers as much as for Tess, to see just how serious they were about each other. Father and son had parted on barely civil terms, and hadn't spoken again until this morning.

'Of course he'll be there,' Piers assured her now. 'And Dee. He's going to fly her down specially.'

'He is?' She blinked at him, then bit her lip. 'Your mother is prepared to leave your aunt...at a time like this? When your aunt's so close to——'

'Look, Aunt Camille could hold on for days yet—weeks, even. She understands that life has to go on. She'll have her permanent nurse with her. And my mother will be back with her by the next day.'

But Tess still wasn't sure. 'But if anything happened the night your mother was down here, she would never forgive herself for not being there with her.' And she'd never forgive me either, she thought heavily. Or Julius wouldn't. 'Couldn't we skip the engagement party, Piers, and just have a small family celebration? We could fly up there...'

'No.' Piers was adamant. 'I want all our friends to be with us. I want to show you off to them and the world. I don't want to hide you away as if——'

'As if your family are ashamed to show me off?' she suggested, sweeping in over him.

'That's not what I——' He broke off impatiently. 'For heaven's sake, Tess, why should they be ashamed of you? You're everything they could want in a daughter. You're beautiful, you're intelligent, you're a fine doctor, you're a lovely, caring person, Tess. Like my mother.'

Tess thought of Julius, who had made it so abundantly plain that she was not one of them. 'We've... been brought up in different worlds...'

He looked down at her with a frown. 'My family are not like that, Tess.' He dropped his voice, even though the proprietor was well out of earshot, having melted discreetly behind a far counter, at Piers's request, to let them make their choice. 'It's the kind of person you are that counts with them, not whether you have a bulging bank account, or a toffy background...'

'Or a father,' she said, without thinking.

His look sharpened. 'Is that what you're worried about, Tess? The fact that you don't

know who your father is? Oh, Tess!' He
swooped his head down and kissed her tenderly on the cheek. 'My father might be an
overbearing bully, and I could throttle him at
times, but he'd never hold a thing like that
against you.'

She didn't believe him, but it was comforting to hear him say it.

'All the same, I don't want——'

Piers touched a finger to her lips. 'Tell you
what...we'll compromise. We'll draw up a
list of select friends we want at our engagement party, and we'll fly them up to
Akama for the weekend.'

She gaped at him. 'Oh, Piers, you can't do
that! Fly them all to your island? Where
would they stay? You can't expect——'

'If necessary, we'll put them up at the
Hamilton Island resort—it's only a hop and
a skip away from Akama. We'll fly them into
the Hamilton Island airport and *Mistique* can
pick them up from there and zip them across
to Akama, where Dee and Julius can join us
on board. They'll be within a few minutes'
reach of the house, if the worst happens. Does
that sound satisfactory?'

'Piers, it sounds wonderful...if your parents agree to it. But it would cost a fortune to fly them all——'

'What are fortunes for?' Piers cut in with an ironic lift of his lip. 'I might as well make use of the Branson millions while I still have access to them.'

'You think...' Tess paused, biting her lip. 'You think that once your father realises you're serious about not going into the business, he'll cut you off?' She peered into his face. 'Will you *mind*, Piers? You're so—so used to having whatever you want. Doing whatever you want.' Flying a plane-load of friends to the Whitsundays for a weekend, for instance, at a mere snap of his fingers.

Piers quirked a rueful eyebrow. 'I see you still have much to learn about me, Tess. I can take it or leave it. My needs are simpler than you think. Give me a boat to sail, a roof over my head, a court case to get my teeth into—and you, my beautiful Tess, and I'll have everything I'll ever want. I can do without the rest—it doesn't mean a thing to me. I've never indulged myself to the extent that you and a lot of other people appear to think. I've always put my head down and worked hard.'

'And played hard,' she teased, thinking of his women, his wicked playboy reputation.

'In my leisure hours, sure, I had some good times,' he conceded, a roguish glint in the black eyes. 'When you're young, and single, and have the means to indulge yourself... well, why not? But it wasn't satisfying—except at a superficial level. I wasn't complete, Tess. I wasn't complete until I met you.' His eyes sobered. 'My wild playboy days are over, Tess. I have other priorities now—new responsibilities to look forward to. And, whether Julius cuts me off or not, we'll be all right, Tess,' he said unworriedly. 'We both have successful careers in our own right.'

'I'm not worried about me—I was worried about you!' she said with spirit. 'But maybe...I don't need to be.' Her eyes held his, her love for him shimmering in the depths, deepening the vivid blue.

He caught her hand and lifted it, and the sapphire and diamonds on her finger sparkled under the bright lights.

'You're happy with this one, then?' he asked. When she nodded, he smilingly pressed her hand to his lips, then turned and beckoned to the beaming proprietor.

That evening they phoned Julius and Dee, who were spending some time together up on the island with Aunt Camille. Dee, who answered the phone, sounded delighted at the news, and insisted on having a word with Tess, telling her how happy she would be to have her in the family. But when Julius came on the line he gave no more than a gruff acknowledgement, following it with a tart comment to his son.

'I think you're rushing into it. But I dare say you know your own mind. You ought to by now.'

'Oh, I know my own mind all right,' Piers said coolly. 'I've never been more sure of anything in my life. We plan to have an engagement party next weekend, Jules,' he said, keen to get down to business. 'We realise it's a bad time for Dee to leave the island right now—which is why Tess very thoughtfully suggested we come up there to you...' But when he went on to outline his idea of flying guests to the Whitsundays to join them for the weekend, Julius erupted.

'Are you crazy? You do realise,' he said in a scathing tone, 'that your aunt is sinking fast? She could die at any moment. She needs calm right now, not excitement!'

'But our friends won't be anywhere near my aunt...' Piers sounded less cool now, his face tight. 'They'll be on board *Mistique*, and after the party we'll see that they're taken back to Hamilton Island, and only Tess and I —— '

'No!' Julius roared. 'I'm not having it! It's a ridiculous idea. It's a blatant waste of money. It's most unlike you, Piers, to be so extravagant!'

Tess, who could hear every word he roared through the phone, felt her heart dip. Obviously Julius was blaming her for Piers's extravagance, since it had been her suggestion to celebrate their engagement on the island. He'd assumed it was also her idea to bring a string of guests with them, and must think she was wasting no time splashing the Branson millions around.

'I don't know why you can't wait,' Julius was shouting. 'If you had any consideration for your aunt, you'd put your engagement off until she's gone. It can't be much longer, poor thing.'

'No...I realise that,' Piers said, holding on to his temper. 'But Aunt Camille would hate us to put it off because of her. She knows how I feel about Tess—I told her when I was up there. She was all for it. It's *her* we're thinking of, Jules. We want to keep her family around her. We want her to see how happy Tess and I are.'

'I said no!' Julius rasped. 'Just knowing you're all up here would agitate her. Anyway, it's impossible. I need *Mistique* to stay down in Sydney for the next few weeks. I've made commitments...'

Tess gave Piers a nudge. 'It's all right, Piers. We can wait, can't we?'

Piers clapped his hand over the mouth-piece. 'No, we can't! Can't you see what he's trying to do?' Moving his hand away, he ground out, 'Then we'll have it down here. I'm not putting it off, Jules. The announcement will be in the papers to-morrow—and I want the engagement party next weekend. If *Mistique*'s not available then, we'll hold it at my place!'

Julius gave an audible sigh. 'So be it. *Mistique*, as it happens, is not booked for next Saturday. Arrange a buffet lunch on board for that day and I'll fly Dee down...assuming nothing happens in the meantime.' He added a warning. 'Just be prepared to have to cancel at the last minute...and attend a funeral instead!'

'I'll take that chance,' Piers muttered, and hung up.

The party on *Mistique* was in full swing, and only one thing was marring Tess's happiness. Julius and Dee hadn't come—or they hadn't shown up yet, at any rate. All the other guests—other than Andrew and her old school-friend Pamela, who'd sent word by mobile phone that they'd been delayed by a problem with the car but were on their way— were already on board, and the Dom Perignon was flowing. But, due to the late arrivals, *Mistique* was still at the Man o' War steps, unable to set off on the planned harbour cruise.

'Maybe Dee's plane is running late,' Tess suggested, her eyes scanning the empty steps yet again.

'They'd have let us know.' Piers's mouth twisted. 'I knew he'd do something like this.'

Tess looked up into the night-dark eyes she loved, and saw a simmering anger in the black depths. 'What do you mean?' she whispered, a knot of fear twisting inside her. Piers knew his father better than she did—knew what he was capable of. If he didn't approve of his son's choice...

Piers shrugged. 'He's got some bee in his bonnet... I don't know what it is, or why.'

'He wanted you to marry Serena,' Tess said with a sigh.

He arched an eyebrow. 'Yeah...maybe. Well, I'm not going to let him spoil today for us, Tess. Nothing's going to spoil it. We'll enjoy ourselves all the more without him.'

Tess chewed on her lip, trying not to fear the worst. 'I'm sure there's some logical explanation,' she said, slipping her arm round him. As she ran a soothing hand over his back and shoulders she felt the tension knotting his muscles, and felt a surge of love, knowing that the anger he was feeling was for her, not for himself. 'Maybe you should call them,' she suggested, kneading the taut muscles at the base of his neck. 'It might be your aunt.'

'If it is, there's nothing we can do,' he said tightly. 'I'm not calling him. The minute your friends Andrew and Pamela turn up, we're off.' He looked down at her, a new tenderness lifting the shadows of resentment from his eyes. 'In the meantime, my darling, shall we go and join the others? It's time we started enjoying ourselves.'

'Sorry I'm late.'

Tess swung round at the sound of Julius Branson's voice. He had appeared without warning, and she felt herself trembling, with an odd sense of foreboding, as she turned and saw that he was alone. His pale blue eyes were hard to read, his face equally impassive, his white hair burnished to a silvery sheen by the bright midday sun. It was Piers, standing beside her, who spoke first, rapping a question at his father.

'Where's Dee?'

Julius met his eye. 'Your mother won't be coming. Your aunt died this morning. That's what delayed me. I've been on the phone...organising things.'

Tess felt Piers exhale a deep breath at her side. 'So you were right,' he conceded in a tight voice. 'We should have waited. That's what you're about to say, isn't it?'

Julius gave a twitch of his lip. 'A bit late to worry about that now. I saw no point in letting you know earlier and giving you the dilemma of deciding whether or not to call off your celebration. There's nothing you can do at this point. The funeral won't be for a couple of days. Your aunt is to be buried on the island, as she wished.'

Tess touched his arm impulsively. 'I'm very sorry, Mr Branson. I know how close you and your wife were to her.'

He glanced down at her, his eyes squinting against the brightness, veiling his expression. 'Thank you. I trust this won't put a dampener on your day.'

Tess gulped, and shook her head, wondering if this was Julius Branson's way of saying he was sorry for the way he had treated her in the past. Or even his way of giving her his blessing at last—but only, no doubt, because he realised he had no choice! But—she eyed him speculatively—he *had* been thoughtful enough not to disrupt their plans for the day. And he *had* turned up himself, when he had a perfect excuse not to.

'Nothing's going to put a dampener on our day,' Piers put in firmly, sliding a hand over Tess's shoulder. He waved to a passing member of the crew, who was flitting round with a bottle of Dom Perignon, filling glasses.

'Are you going to drink a toast to us, Jules?'
he challenged.

Before his father could answer, a figure
flashed between them, a dark-haired woman
in a flowing trouser-suit in shades of taupe
and cream. She hurled herself at Tess.

'Tess, old thing, I'm so happy for you! Let
me see your ring!' She snatched Tess's hand.

'Pamela! What on earth happened to your
car?' Tess smiled in relief. 'I thought you
weren't going to make it. Oh, never mind
that...' She turned laughingly to Piers. 'This
is the Pamela you've heard so much about.
My oldest and most talented friend. She's a
brilliant architect. *And* a glorious violinist,
who plays sometimes for the Sydney
Symphony Orchestra.'

'And you remember me, old man?' Andrew
thrust himself forward, hand outstretched,
ready to pump his old rival's hand. 'You did
me a favour, you know, Piers, old fellow,
stealing Tess away from me...' He turned and
winked at Pamela, and Tess was relieved to
see the genuine affection and happiness in his
eyes, all trace of the old animosity gone.

As Piers turned away from him to have a word with Pamela Andrew stepped over to Tess to give her a brief hug.

'Well, Tess, you've finally got what you wanted,' he said, and though his tone was teasing rather than spiteful, Tess felt a twinge of guilt at the reminder of the deliberate way she had set out to catch Piers Branson's eye the first time she had stepped aboard *Mistique* . . . and the way she had used him to get to his father. If only she were at liberty to tell Piers the truth, and get it off her chest!

As she glanced past Andrew's shoulder she saw Julius Branson watching her, and knew in that instant that he couldn't have failed to hear what Andrew had said. She felt her heart sink, knowing it would only confirm what he already thought of her. She faced him defiantly, her eyes telling him proudly that she loved his son for the man he was, not for his money or his name or his possessions, and that he could jolly well think what he liked!

She felt a tiny jolt when she saw a question in the pale blue eyes rather than condemnation, a softening rather than a hardening. And then he turned away.

She was left shaken. Was Julius beginning to realise at last how much she loved Piers? Finally getting used to the idea of his son marrying a woman he would never approve of, would never have chosen himself?

As the sun sank behind vermilion-streaked clouds, *Mistique* cruised back to the Man o' War steps, where the guests made their farewells and began drifting ashore. Tess felt a hand on her arm, and looked up to see Julius Branson.

'Come down below with me,' he said. 'I want to talk to you.'

She felt her throat constrict. Surely he wasn't contemplating making another attempt to buy her off? A last-ditch attempt to get her out of their lives? She glanced quickly around for Piers, but he was engrossed with the last group of guests at the gangway and had his back to her.

'Piers can join us later,' Julius said. She could read nothing in his face. 'Come on...come with me.' He tugged her away.

All the way down to the sumptuous private quarters on the lowest level, where he led her, her mind was in a fever of speculation. Would he dare try it again? Had he only held back until now, waiting for the death of poor Camille, because he hadn't wanted to cause her any possible distress in her last days, knowing how close his son had always been to his Aunt Camille—and how happy she had been for him? Yes . . . it would have distressed her to see them torn apart.

'Sit down,' Julius invited, leading her across the room. It was a library—a private reading-room. There were a few comfortable chairs, a neat book-case covering one entire wall, and a modern desk.

'I'd prefer to stand,' she said, jutting out her chin. Easier, she thought, to make a dash for it, if necessary.

'As you wish.' Julius drew in his breath. His face, she thought, showed strain. 'I'm free at last to tell you something I've had to hold back . . . for too many years. The truth about your father.'

It was so unexpected that she had to clutch the back of a chair for support.

'You're—you're saying you *are* my father after all?' she croaked. Shock and dismay washed over her. How would this affect her relationship with Piers? It would finish it!

They couldn't both have the same father...even if Piers was not Julius Branson's real son. By legally adopting him, Julius had *made* him his son. In the eyes of the law, she and Piers would be brother and sister!

She gave a muffled sob. No wonder Julius had been trying to break them up! He was only telling her now because he saw no other way!

'I'm not your father,' Julius was quick to reassure her. 'I told you before that I wasn't. But it *was* someone close to me. Your father was my older brother, Simon... Camille's husband.'

She stared at him, her lips parting. 'You mean...the husband who died?' she asked stupidly.

'He died some years ago...yes. He was killed in a freak accident, during a gruelling Sydney-to-Hobart yacht race—the worst on record. Camille was devastated. They were very close.'

She could barely take it in. 'You're saying that my mother——'

'Had an affair with him. Barely even that— a brief one-night encounter, during a conference the three of us were attending. When your mother told him later that she was pregnant, Simon confided in me.' Julius's tone was gruff, though the hard edge had gone. 'He said it had happened at a time of intense stress for both of them. Your mother was deeply depressed because her husband was refusing to give her the child she wanted. My brother was feeling equally low, having just learned that his wife, whom he loved dearly, could never have children. In comforting each other...well, these things happen. Both were in a vulnerable state. Not for us to condemn,' he muttered with a sigh.

Tess looked at him, almost with pity, sensing how difficult it must be for him to tell her all this. She moistened her dry lips. 'And when he found out that she was expecting his child...?' *Me*, she thought painfully as she left the question hanging.

'Your mother confided in Simon before she told her husband. My brother, having despaired of ever having a child, was elated and distressed at the same time. He immediately thought of Camille, whom he loved more than life. She'd always been a fragile little thing, easily hurt. He knew that if she found out he'd had a child by another woman it would destroy her. Destroy them both. Your mother—Rosalind—assured him that she and her husband loved each other dearly, and that he was bound to accept her child, once it was born...even knowing it wasn't his. My brother, naturally, offered to help them—generously—on condition that your mother keep his name a close secret, even from her husband, for as long as Camille lived. She wasn't even to tell *you*, Tess. My brother was thinking of poor Camille—his beloved wife—who was already desolated because she couldn't have any children of her own. You must try to forgive him, Tess,' Julius appealed to her, taking a step towards her.

Tess looked up at him, her eyes misty with unshed tears. 'So that's why you couldn't tell me,' she whispered. 'But...your brother died years ago. And yet his money still kept on coming. Did *you* send it, Mr Branson?' she asked, meeting him eye to eye.

He gave a brief nod. 'My brother had a premonition when he went into that yacht race. Or maybe he was just taking wise precautions, knowing how dangerous the race can be. He told me that, if anything should happen to him, the regular payments he was sending to you and your mother were to continue—and he made me swear to keep his secret for as long as his wife was alive. Camille's feelings and well-being, he said, had to come before anything else.' His eyes were pained, apologetic, as they met hers.

She gulped. 'At least I know now why you acted the way you did...when I accused *you* of being my father. No wonder you wanted to be rid of me! I threatened the peace of your sister-in-law's last days—at least in your mind. You didn't know me—I understand that,' she said gently. 'You couldn't take a chance on my keeping quiet about it, once I knew the truth.'

A muscle twitched at his jaw. 'No, I didn't know you—not then. I didn't dare tell you the truth, or even show any reaction to you when we first met—not with Camille in the house, and her health so delicate. And I confess that I did have certain reservations about you at first—about what you wanted from us,' he admitted heavily. 'I had to ask myself—were you only after money? After what you considered rightfully yours? Had you only been using Piers...to get to me? Or wcre you hoping to get him to marry you, so that you could get hold of your inheritance the easy way? At that time, you understand,' he said contritely, 'I didn't think Piers was serious about you—since he'd never been serious about any other woman in his life, never shown any sign of wanting to settle down. I didn't think he'd care too deeply, or for long.'

Tess nodded slowly. 'So you told me you weren't my father—which was true—and offered me a small fortune to get rid of me.'

'Right.' He sighed. 'I had to keep you away from Camille. One look at you—at your hair, your eyes, your mannerisms—and she could have guessed. Simon's hair, when she first met him, was the same rich red as yours—far redder than mine ever was—only his faded to grey even quicker than mine did.' He spread his hands. 'And I was afraid, too, that Piers might already have mentioned to Camille that your mother had once worked for me...and so could also have known Simon. Poor Camille could very easily have put two and two together.'

'Yes—yes, I see.' It all made sense now. Everything.

'And later,' Julius went on sombrely, 'when I realised you *were* both serious about each other, I tried my best to get you to wait— knowing that Camille couldn't have much longer. Because I knew that the moment you got engaged, Piers would want to take you to meet her. My dear...' He caught her hand, and crushed it in his own. 'I'm bitterly ashamed of the way I've treated you. I realised very quickly that you weren't after our money—that you hadn't sought us out for what you could get out of us. You came to us out of a perfectly natural need to know the truth—to know your origins, your family. I'm ashamed I ever thought it might be anything else.'

'Well, well, well,' drawled a voice from the door, and Tess spun round, her hand slipping from Julius's grasp.

'Piers!' she breathed, her throat tightening at the sight of him. There was a frightening tautness about him, a withering anger in his black eyes as he strode across the room to face her.

'So...it was no accident that we met, Tess? No accident that you caught my eye that day—and spent the rest of the week making sure I was hooked!' He didn't touch her, his body as stiff as his face, rejecting her, shutting her out. 'You planned, from the moment we met, to use me—to string me along. How the hell did I never see it? The warning signs were all there—all those insidious questions about Julius Branson, the mock admiration for the way we lived—for everything we did. If it *was* a pretence!' he scoffed, his eyes bitter.

'How—how long have you been standing there, eavesdropping?' she accused, attack seeming the best way to deal with the situation. She would hardly deny it—she *had* used him!

'Long enough to hear all I wanted to hear— or *didn't* want to hear!' he bit back with crushing scorn. He took a step closer, and she flinched under the scalding fury in his eyes, even though she sensed that his anger was only a cover for the deep hurt he must be feeling underneath. 'You never wanted me—I was only a means to an end. You just wanted to use me to get to my father... and keep on using me until you'd managed to drag an admission from him! Well, now you have... You're a Branson. A *real* one, unlike Phoebe and me. Why don't you go ahead and claim

your birthright—the precious Branson millions?' he lashed out at her. 'You don't need
me any more to get your hands on your
inheritance!'

She felt a knife-stab of hurt. But rather than
wilting under his tongue-lashing—she wasn't
a redhead for nothing—she hid her hurt and
lashed right back.

'And what about you?' she fumed. 'Why
did you chase after *me* in the beginning?
Because you wanted me in your bed! You even
warned me not to expect a meaningful relationship! And why did you *persist* in chasing
after me? Because you found me an irresistible challenge—because I wouldn't tumble
into your bed at a snap of your fingers!'

She saw something shimmer in his eyes, but
didn't stop.

'And if I'd wanted the Branson millions,'
she hissed at him, 'do you think I'd have been
backing up your plan to stick with your law
career, knowing it could mean we'd be giving
up everything, knowing we could be cut off
without a——' She clapped a hand to her
mouth in dismay, realising that Julius was still
in the room, and could hear every word.

She was astonished when he merely waved a resigned hand, and said calmly, as Piers swung round to face him, 'I've always been aware of your ambition, son. You've told me often enough, but I refused to take you seriously. I hoped it was just a passing whim—a way of keeping your brain sharp, because the family business wasn't giving you enough responsibility or challenge with me still at the helm. But if you really want to devote yourself solely to the law——'

'I do,' Piers said firmly. 'I'll still be prepared to give legal advice, as I've told you before, Jules. I'm not turning my back on the family business—far from it. And I'll still sit on the board as a non-executive director, and keep my shares in the business, if you still want me to. But Phoebe and Tom are perfectly capable of running the business—the whole shebang—and running it well. Without me. It's what they both want.'

Julius inclined his head. 'Then so be it,' he said with a sigh. 'I won't stand in your way. A man knows when he's beaten.' He glanced from his son to Tess, and now there was a warmer expression in his eyes than mere resignation. 'I'll leave you two to work things out—I'm confident you will.' And his lip actually twitched as he turned and left them, as if he knew that the deep love they felt for each other would heal whatever hurt and anger they were feeling now.

Left alone, they turned back to face each other, both still tense, wary. Their eyes met, black clashing with blue, pride fighting pride. The look lengthened, and then subtly changed, a tiny spark of humour glowing in the black, an answering gleam brightening the blue.

'I guess we both had hidden motives...in the beginning,' Piers conceded, a wry smile tugging at the corners of his mouth.

Her lips quivered. 'But only in the beginning. Until...' Her eyes sobered, her love for him darkening the vivid blue. 'Until what I felt for you changed everything. Piers...' She gazed earnestly up at him. 'When I found out, while I was at Akama, that Julius wasn't my father, I was *relieved*, not disappointed. Because it meant that I could... That my feelings for you could——'

'I know,' Piers broke in gently, a smouldering passion burning the laughter from his eyes. 'Whatever motives we might have had in the beginning, you and I, our feelings for each other—the love that grew between us—swept everything else aside. That's all that matters, Tess—the way we feel about each other now. From this day on.'

'You mean . . .' Her eyes searched his face. 'You forgive me for the way I —— '

'Hush.' His hands reached for her shoulders, his fingers closing round them. 'There's nothing to forgive. Look at it this way, Tess . . .' A wicked gleam livened the black eyes. 'Our initial motives—your search for your father, and my—OK, I admit it—my lecherous intentions towards a certain gorgeous redhead—are what brought us together. And kept us together until we knew that was where we belonged. So we ought to be grateful to our ulterior motives for bringing an unlikely pair together. Now come here . . .' He dragged her into his arms. 'I love you, Tess Keneally. And I don't intend to let you forget it . . . ever.'

Throwing her back against one arm, almost sweeping her off her feet, he reached out with his other arm and locked the door. 'Just in case you doubt me,' he murmured, nuzzling his face into the creamy silk of her throat, 'I intend to start showing you right here and now.'

EPILOGUE

TESS sat on the sun-drenched balcony of her harbourside home, watching the colourful yachts and decorated ferries on the harbour. Another Australia Day—the second anniversary of her first meeting with Piers. She wished he would hurry home.

She leaned on her arms, hugging her secret. His plane was due in around four o'clock from Singapore, where he'd been for the past five days at a legal conference, and at the same time settling some deal on behalf of one of his father's companies. It was the longest they'd ever been apart.

Tonight she planned to have a romantic candlelit dinner at home, just for the two of them. The dining-room table, overlooking the harbour through their vast picture windows, was already set with the best silver and crystal and her finest embroidered linen. The champagne was chilling in the fridge, the smoked salmon starter prepared, the pot-roast—Piers's favourite—simmering on the stove, and her own home-baked apple pie, another of his favourites, ready to reheat. There was nothing more she needed to do until the last minute.

She scanned the boats on the harbour, looking for *Mistique*. Would Piers mind Olivia not being here when he got home? Dee had taken their seven-month-old daughter on board the big yacht for the day, so that she and Piers could be alone. Dee loved looking after her. On the three mornings a week that Tess went in to her consulting-rooms, she had no qualms about leaving the baby with either Dee or with Honey, their warm-hearted housekeeper. The Honeys had stayed on at the Bransons' big old family home on the harbour when she and Piers had moved in. Julius and Dee had wanted a smaller place as their Sydney base, and had ended up taking over Piers's apartment next door. They had virtually swapped homes! Phoebe and Tom, both still as career-minded as ever and happily married now too, had been perfectly content to stay in their existing apartment. They all shared the tennis-court and the pool below the old family home, and they all got on well.

Tess sat up as she saw *Mistique* cruising past, waving as she saw Dee holding Olivia aloft. And was that Phoebe standing next to her? The family knew what she'd planned for the evening. But... She felt a faint stir of disquiet. What if Piers's plane was delayed? What if he'd missed it altogether, and didn't arrive home in time to celebrate this special evening with her? He'd made no mention of the Australia Day holiday when he'd called her last night from Singapore to say he hoped to be home by late afternoon the next day. Had he been so busy with his legal conference and his other legal work that he'd forgotten what day it was in Australia?

It wasn't like Piers, though, not to make any mention of a looming anniversary. He was normally so good that way—a true romantic, keen to celebrate not only birthdays and wedding anniversaries, but any other special event in their lives. Making *her* feel special. Special, and wanted, and much loved.

Last year they had celebrated the Australia Day holiday with his family and a few of their closest friends on board *Mistique*, just as they had on the day they first met. She had been four months pregnant then with Olivia.

Today, though, she had declined the family's invitation to join them on the harbour, and they'd understood, knowing that she wanted to be home when Piers arrived. Not that they had any idea yet—she moved her hand down to stroke her still-flat stomach—that this anniversary was...extra special.

But—she chewed on her lip—was Piers going to be home in time to celebrate this special Australia Day anniversary with her? If his plane was delayed and didn't get in until this evening, would he *feel* like a romantic candlelit dinner after the long flight from Singapore? Maybe he would just want to flop into bed and go to sleep. If he arrived home at all...

For all she knew, he could have decided to catch a later plane, overlooking the fact that it was a special day. Or not thinking it important enough any more...

She heaved a deep sigh. Was this what happened after a year and a half of marriage? Was this the beginning of the end of the honeymoon? Did complacency set in? Or was she just feeling a bit emotional and insecure because she was pregnant again? The doctor had confirmed it yesterday. Would Piers be

happy about it? Or would he think it was too
soon? When the new baby arrived, Olivia
would still be in nappies!

When the doorbell rang she jumped up in
relief. But halfway to the door she faltered.
Why would Piers ring the bell when he had
his own key? Had Pamela and Andrew decided to drop in, knowing that she was on her
own?

Pulling open the door, she saw the red roses
before she noticed the delivery girl holding
them. She felt her heart dive to her toes. He
wasn't coming—he'd sent flowers instead!

She carried them inside. She'd never seen
so many red roses in her life. They were
covered with clear cellophane, and there was
a white envelope pinned to the cellophane.
She carefully laid the roses down on the
nearest table and tore the envelope open.

Instead of a card inside, there was a folded
letter. She blinked when she saw it was from
Piers. A hand-written letter! Now, how...?

She sank into a chair to read it.

My darling Tess,
A friend I met in Singapore is delivering
this letter to the florist in Sydney, since he'll
be arriving on an earlier plane. I didn't want

to fax it—that didn't seem the right thing to do.

These roses are for you, my love, on this special day—the second anniversary of the first day we met. Australia Day, the day that changed my life, changed me. A day I will never forget, Tess, because it brought me you. My dearest, in these past two perfect years, and especially since we have been married, you have given me so much. Your love, your companionship, your wisdom, your humour, your loving support, and, of course, the greatest gift of all, our beautiful daughter Olivia, who looks more like her mother each day. Tess, you are my best friend, my lover, my life.

When I spoke to you last night on the phone, did you think I might have forgotten what day it was? It was wicked of me to tease you, but I wanted to surprise you with this letter and the roses. Do you realise—a big admission!—that this is the first love-letter I've ever written? And I've never sent *red* roses to any other woman but you, Tess. To me, they symbolise love.

If you're wondering why I'm writing to you when I'll have you in my arms again in a few hours, well, sometimes it's easier to put into writing what's in a man's heart than to say it face to face. Then if it sounds corny I won't have to watch you laughing at me. We laugh a lot, you and I, Tess. We always did share a healthy sense of humour, cracking up over things that a lot of people would find deadly serious. At the risk of being laughed at, I'll dare to say a few words more.

Tess, I'm missing you so much. I've missed you every second of these past five days and five long nights. Especially the nights. I miss the feel of your skin under my fingers, the sound of your husky voice, the sublime heights we reach together. And above all I miss your lovely face, those kissable lips, that glorious hair that I love to run my fingers through.

Tess, I'm missing you both—so much. Have you missed me, my love? Has Olivia, I wonder, missed me too? I truly hope I haven't missed out on anything new and amazing that our daughter has done since I've been away. She changes so quickly, grows so quickly.

When I come home, Tess, let's make

another baby? Let's have lots of babies. A boy next time, perhaps? But another beautiful girl would be just as wonderful.

I should be home around five. If you've planned a celebratory dinner out tonight, Tess, cancel it. Let's stay at home. We could phone for a pizza and eat it sitting out on the balcony under the stars, watching the fireworks on the harbour. And then, Tess, let's have an early night???

Kiss Olivia for me. I love you both, forever and beyond.

Your loving husband,
Piers.

MILLS & BOON NOW PUBLISH
EIGHT LARGE PRINT TITLES A MONTH.
THESE ARE THE EIGHT NEW TITLES
FOR JANUARY 1996

PRINCE OF LIES
Robyn Donald

THE ONE AND ONLY
Carole Mortimer

CHRIS
Sally Wentworth

TO CATCH A PLAYBOY
Elizabeth Duke

DANGEROUS DECEIVER
Lindsay Armstrong

PROMISE OF PASSION
Natalie Fox

DARK PIRATE
Angela Devine

HEARTLESS PURSUIT
Jessica Steele

MILLS & BOON NOW PUBLISH
EIGHT LARGE PRINT TITLES A MONTH.
THESE ARE THE EIGHT NEW TITLES
FOR FEBRUARY 1996

CRIME OF PASSION
Lynne Graham

A BITTERSWEET PROMISE
Grace Green

THE MAN WHO BROKE HEARTS
Stephanie Howard

WILD HUNGER
Charlotte Lamb

A HAUNTING OBSESSION
Miranda Lee

THE LOVE TRAP
Emma Richmond

FRANCESCA
Sally Wentworth

RETURN TO SENDER
Rebecca Winters